MW00635489

THE ULTIMATE
SAINT. LOUIS BLUES
TRIVIA BOOK

A Collection of Amazing Trivia Quizzes
and Fun Facts for Die-Hard Blues Fans!

Ray Walker

978-1-953563-29-3

Copyright © 2020 by HRP House

ALL RIGHTS RESERVED

No part of this book may be reproduced, stored in a retrieval system, or transmitted in any form or by any means, electronic, mechanical, photocopying, recording, scanning, or otherwise, without the prior written permission of the publisher.

Exclusive Free Book

Crazy Sports Stories

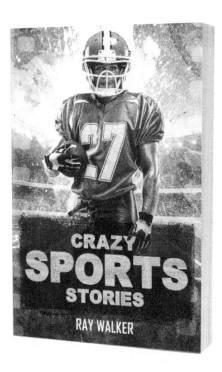

As a thank you for getting a copy of this book I would like to offer you a free copy of my book Crazy Sports Stories which comes packed with interesting stories from your favorite sports such as Football, Hockey, Baseball, Basketball and more.

Grab your free copy over at
RayWalkerMedia.com/Bonus

CONTENTS

INTRODUCTION

The St. Louis Blues have been survivors, if nothing else, ever since joining the NHL back in 1967-68. The club's determination and never-say-die attitude has enabled it to fight through tough financial times and what seemed like almost certain relocation in the past.

Happily, the Blues are still in St. Louis and, even though they may have been the last of the 1967 expansion teams to win the Stanley Cup, they're the reigning and defending champions in 2019-20.

The city hosted an NHL franchise back in the 1930s for one season and finally returned to the league three decades later. The Blues have been one of the most consistent teams ever since with a remarkable number of playoff appearances, including a streak of 25 straight seasons.

Loyal fans and a new owner helped keep the organization in St. Louis in the 1980s when it looked as if the Blues were headed to Canada. Their incredible playoff streak began soon after and the Stanley Cup was eventually hoisted just over half a century after the club's inaugural season.

Fans have been fortunate enough to see several famous Hockey Hall-of-Famers skate or tend goal for the team over the years. These include Jacques Plante, Glenn Hall, Brett Hull, Bernie Federko, Al MacInnis, Chris Pronger, and a brief stint by "The Great One" himself, Wayne Gretzky.

This St. Louis Blues trivia fact book contains an abundance of information about the Blues franchise from the very first game to the conclusion of the 2019-20 regular NHL season.

The book contains 15 different chapters, each of which features 15 multiple-choice questions and five true-or-false statements, with the correct answers revealed on the following page. Each chapter also provides ten interesting "Did You Know" facts and anecdotes concerning the team.

Blues' supporters can re-live the ups and downs of the franchise and perhaps learn something new while they're at it. The trivia book will help you prepare to challenge family members, friends, and fellow fans in trivia showdowns.

When asked what have the Blues done lately? Passionate fans like yourself can proudly say, "They won the Stanley Cup in 2019."

Hopefully, this trivia fact book will help you realize why you're such a loyal St. Louis Blues fan.

CHAPTER 1:

ORIGINS & HISTORY

QUIZ TIME!

1. When St. Louis was awarded the Blues, what was the seating capacity of the St. Louis Arena?

    a. 10,000

    b. 15,000

    c. 18,000

    d. 12,000

2. When did the Blues play their first NHL season?

    a. 1970-71

    b. 1974-75

    c. 1967-68

    d. 1972-73

3. Lynn Patrick was the Blues' first head coach and general manager.

    a. True

    b. False

4. How many times did St. Louis fail to make the playoffs in their first 51 seasons?

   a. 9
   b. 10
   c. 13
   d. 7

5. How many combined regulation and overtime/shootout losses did the Blues suffer in 2005-06?

   a. 57
   b. 49
   c. 61
   d. 45

6. Who replaced Lynn Patrick as head coach midway through their first season?

   a. Al Arbour
   b. Scotty Bowman
   c. Sid Abel
   d. Lou Angotti

7. How many times did the club qualify for the playoffs between 1980 and 2004?

   a. 20
   b. 18
   c. 19
   d. 25

8. St. Louis appeared in the Stanley Cup finals in its first four seasons in the NHL.

a. True

b. False

9. How many of their 74 games did the Blues win in their inaugural season?

    a. 30

    b. 27

    c. 29

    d. 32

10. The Blues made their NHL debut against which fellow expansion team?

    a. Los Angeles Kings

    b. Philadelphia Flyers

    c. Minnesota North Stars

    d. Pittsburgh Penguins

11. The team was named after the W.C. Handy song, "St. Louis Blues."

    a. True

    b. False

12. Who was the team's first owner?

    a. R. Hal Dean

    b. Stan Musial

    c. James D. Norris

    d. Sid Salomon Jr.

13. The Blues broke the 100-point barrier for the first time in 1980-81 with how many points?

a. 103

b. 101

c. 104

d. 107

14. The Blues were nearly relocated to Saskatoon, Saskatchewan in the 1980s.

    a. True

    b. False

15. When did St. Louis play its first Winter Classic game?

    a. 2015-16

    b. 2016-17

    c. 2017-18

    d. 2018-19

16. Who was the first player ever drafted by the club in 1968?

    a. Right-winger Vic Teal

    b. Center Bob Collyard

    c. Goaltender Gary Edwards

    d. Left-winger Curt Bennett

17. What year did the team leave the St. Louis Arena for new digs?

    a. 1994

    b. 1993

    c. 1995

    d. 1997

18. For how many seasons did St. Louis play in the Norris Division?

    a. 6
    b. 8
    c. 10
    d. 12

19. Who did the Blues defeat to win their first NHL game?

    a. Toronto Maple Leafs
    b. Pittsburgh Penguins
    c. Chicago Blackhawks
    d. Oakland Seals

20. For the Blues' first three seasons, Jack Buck served as the team's play-by-play announcer.

    a. True
    b. False

QUIZ ANSWERS

1. D – 12,000

2. C – 1967-68

3. A – True

4. A – 9

5. C – 61

6. B – Scotty Bowman

7. D – 24

8. B – False

9. B – 27

10. C – Minnesota North Stars

11. A – True

12. D – Sid Salomon Jr.

13. D – 107

14. A – True

15. B – 2016-17

16. C – Goaltender Gary Edwards

17. A – 1994

18. D – 12

19. B – Pittsburgh Penguins

20. B – False

DID YOU KNOW?

1. The St. Louis Blues NHL franchise is based in the city of St. Louis and the state of Missouri. The club currently competes in the Central Division of the Western Conference. The franchise was granted in 1966 and made its debut in the 1967-68 season, along with five other expansion teams as the league doubled in size from six to 12. The Blues' minor league affiliate is the Springfield Thunderbirds of the American Hockey League (AHL).

2. The Blues franchise is named after a song called "St. Louis Blues" that was originally composed and performed by American musician William Christopher Handy and published in 1914. The hockey club plays its home games at the Enterprise Center in downtown St. Louis. The club played from 1967 to 1994 in the St. Louis Arena before moving to the Enterprise Center.

3. The St. Louis Arena was the second-largest indoor entertainment complex in America next to New York City's Madison Square Garden when it first opened in 1929. The rink, known as the Checkerdome between 1977 and 1983, was demolished in 1999. The Chicago Blackhawks of the NHL occasionally played games in the arena between 1953 and 1959.

4. The Enterprise Center was originally named the Kiel Center when it opened on Oct. 8, 1994. The name

changed to the Savvis Center between 2000 and 2006 and it was then called the Scottrade Center from 2006 to 2018. The name was changed to the Enterprise Center in mid-2018. The arena and the hockey franchise are owned by SLB Acquisition Holdings, LLC, with Thomas H. Stillman being the majority owner of a 16-person consortium.

5. The St. Louis Eagles were the first NHL team to play in the city; they competed for one season in 1934-35. The Eagles franchise was originally founded as the Ottawa Senators in 1883 and joined the NHL in 1917. The club halted operations in 1931-32 due to financial difficulty, moved to St. Louis in 1934, and folded after the season.

6. The Blues were the last of the 1967 expansion teams to be granted a franchise by the NHL. They can thank the Chicago Blackhawks they were chosen ahead of Baltimore. The Blackhawk owners also owned the St. Louis Arena and convinced the NHL to award a team to the city even though it reportedly hadn't submitted a formal bid.

7. The first owners of the Blues were Sid Salomon Jr., his son Sid Salomon III, and Robert L. Wolfson. The original investment group also included former St. Louis Cardinals baseball star Stan Musial. When the franchise was granted, the owners had to purchase the then-decrepit St. Louis Arena from the Chicago Blackhawks and expand its seating capacity to 15,000 from 12,000.

8. The Blues came close to folding or being relocated in the early to mid-1970s because of financial distress and the competing World Hockey Association (WHA). Team president Emile Francis managed to convince pet food company Ralston Purina to buy the team and arena in 1977. Purina lost interest in the team in 1983 and the franchise was forfeited to the NHL. It came close to relocating to Saskatoon, Saskatchewan, but Harry Ornest bought the club and kept it in St. Louis. He then sold is after the 1985-86 season to Michael Shanahan and his group.

9. Walmart heir Nancy Walton Laurie bought the Blues with her husband Bill in 1999 and sold the franchise in 2005 to a company called SCP Worldwide. However, the sale fell through and the club began negotiations with General Sports and Entertainment, LLC. The team was eventually bought by SCP and TowerBrook Capital Partners in 2006 and sold to SLB Acquisition Holdings in 2012.

10. The Blues have failed to make the playoffs just nine times as of 2019 and in 1980 they kicked off a run of 25 straight post-season appearances. The team has played in four Stanley Cup finals and hoisted the trophy for the first time in 2019. Their 42 post-season appearances are the most for any team other than "The Original Six" of Boston, Detroit, Montreal, Toronto, Chicago, and the New York Rangers. However, they were the last of the 1967 expansion teams to win the Stanley Cup.

CHAPTER 2:

JERSEYS & NUMBERS

QUIZ TIME!

1. How many numbers has St. Louis retired as of 2020?

    a. 5

    b. 7

    c. 9

    d. 6

2. Bob Gassoff was the first player to have his number retired by the club. What number did he wear?

    a. 4

    b. 2

    c. 3

    d. 5

3. The No. 7 has been honored, but not retired, for three different players.

    a. True

    b. False

4. Which number has never been worn by a Blues' player as of 2020?

    a. 75
    b. 86
    c. 20
    d. 52

5. Which is not an official team color of the Blues?

    a. Navy blue
    b. Royal blue
    c. Black
    d. White

6. When did the Blues introduce their first alternate jersey?

    a. 1997-98
    b. 1998-99
    c. 1996-97
    d. 1999-2000

7. From 1994 to 1998, what image did the team wear on their shoulder crest?

    a. Gateway Arch
    b. Trumpet
    c. The primary logo
    d. Nothing

8. No. 19 was worn by 11 different players between 1970 and 1975.

    a. True
    b. False

9. What number did Brett Hull wear for 10 years in St. Louis?

    a. 17

    b. 22

    c. 15

    d. 16

10. Alex Pietrangelo wears which number for the Blues?

    a. 32

    b. 17

    c. 29

    d. 27

11. The logo on St. Louis' jersey is known as the "Blue Note."

    a. True

    b. False

12. Who was the first St. Louis player to wear No. 3?

    a. Brent Hughes

    b. Andre Dupont

    c. Al Arbour

    d. Fran Huck

13. How many players have worn No. 12 in St. Louis?

    a. 40

    b. 34

    c. 28

    d. 35

14. Between 2007 and 2017, the numbers on the club's home jersey were colored gold.

    a. True
    b. False

15. Who was the first Blues' player to wear No. 48?

    a. Ladislav Nagy
    b. Scott Young
    c. Dale Clarke
    d. Petteri Linbohm

16. T.J. Oshie wore this number from 2008-09 to 2014-15.

    a. 74
    b. 65
    c. 77
    d. 54

17. What color was introduced on the team's jersey in 1985-86?

    a. Purple
    b. Orange
    c. Red
    d. Navy blue

18. The retired No. 5 belongs to which Blues alumnus?

    a. Barclay Plager
    b. Red Berenson
    c. Bob Plager
    d. Al MacInnis

19. What number does goaltender Jordan Binnington wear?

    a. 39
    b. 60
    c. 70
    d. 50

20. From 2008 to 2016, the Blues' alternate jersey featured the Missouri Botanical Garden surrounding the blue note on the crest.

    a. True
    b. False

QUIZ ANSWERS

1. B – 7

2. C – 3

3. B – False

4. D – 52

5. C – Black

6. A – 1997-98

7. B – Trumpet

8. A – True

9. D – 16

10. D – 27

11. A – True

12. C – Al Arbour

13. B – 34

14. A – True

15. B – Scott Young

16. A – 74

17. C – Red

18. C – Bob Plager

19. D – 50

20. B – False

DID YOU KNOW?

1. The Blues' two primary jerseys are predominantly blue with gold-and-white trimming and white with blue-and-gold trimming. The jersey's front crest features a blue winged musical note emblem. Their regular uniforms also consist of either blue socks with white-and-gold trim or white socks with blue-and-gold trim along with black pants.

2. The club changed its look in the mid-1980s when red was added to the uniform and the shade of blue was darkened. The name "St. Louis" was also added to the crest above the musical note for several years and was then removed. In 1994-95 the color red was more prominent and a trumpet logo was briefly added to the shoulders of the jersey.

3. A new alternate white jersey was introduced in 1997 and the original lighter shade of blue was brought back. In addition, the red areas were replaced with navy blue. A year later, a similarly styled blue jersey was introduced.

4. The Blues had planned on a third jersey in 2007 with navy blue and a new logo that contained a graphic of the city's famous Gateway Arch inside a circle that had the blue note superimposed over. The word "St. Louis" was above it and the "Blues" was below it. The jersey was first used on Nov. 21, 2008.

5. In 2014-15, the organization tweaked the jerseys again, returning to the look of 1998 to 2007. However, the navy blue third jersey wasn't changed but it was discontinued in 2016. The team brought out a new third jersey for 2018-19 that was based on the design of the 2017 Winter Classic jersey.

6. As of 2020, the Blues have retired seven jersey numbers. These belonged to defensemen Al MacInnis (2), Bob Gassoff (3), Bob Plager (5), and Barclay Plager (8) and forwards Brian Sutter (11), Brett Hull (16), and Bernie Federko (24). The No. 99, which was worn by Wayne Gretzky, was also retired by the NHL.

7. The Blues have announced that blue-liner Chris Pronger's No. 44 will be retired in a ceremony sometime during the 2020-21 season. In addition, the No. 7, which was worn by Garry Unger, Red Berenson, Joe Mullen, and Keith Tkachuk has been honored with a mural of the players at the Enterprise Center. Doug Wickenheiser's No. 14 is no longer issued by the team and there's a banner at the arena recognizing it.

8. Center Doug Wickenheiser played with the Blues from 1983-84 to 1986-87 and passed away from cancer at the age of 37 in St. Louis in 1999. While his number is no longer issued by the club, it was worn by six different players after he left the team in 1987. However, it hasn't been worn since 2002.

9. The most popular jersey in team history so far has been the No. 12, which has been worn by 34 players as of

2020. Those who have donned the number include Dickie Moore, Terry Crisp, Noel Picard, Claude Larose, Joe Micheletti, Ron Flockhart, Adam Oates, Dale Hawerchuk, and Kevin Shattenkirk. The most recent to wear it is Zach Sanford in 2019-20.

10. Every jersey number between 1 and 51 has been worn by at least one player, with 99 being the highest worn. The supposedly "unlucky" No. 13 was worn by seven players: Yuri Khmylev, Ray Ferraro, Valeri Bure, Bill Guerin, Dan Hinote, and Carlo Colaiacovo. Olli Jokinen was the last to wear it, in 2015.

CHAPTER 3:

FAMOUS QUOTES

QUIZ TIME!

1. Which former Blues star stated, "I'm scared to death to fly commercial... I have not flown commercial since 9/11"?

    a. Adam Oates
    b. Wayne Gretzky
    c. Brett Hull
    d. T.J. Oshie

2. "Maybe it wasn't the talent the Lord gave me—maybe it was the passion," was spoken by which player?

    a. Jordan Binnington
    b. Ryan O'Reilly
    c. Wayne Gretzky
    d. Red Berenson

3. When Brett Hull heard he was being traded to St. Louis, he responded, "I hope it's someplace nice."

    a. True

b. False

4. Which player said, "I think he knows all my tricks. Or the fact I don't have any tricks."

   a. Brendan Shanahan
   b. Shayne Corson
   c. Brian Sutter
   d. Bernie Federko

5. When asked why he played 36 holes of golf, which player answered, "Because there wasn't enough time to play 54"?

   a. Grant Fuhr
   b. Garry Unger
   c. Alex Pietrangelo
   d. Tyler Bozak

6. "A happy player is a good player, I think," was said by which Blues' goalie?

   a. Jacques Plante
   b. Glenn Hall
   c. Jordan Binnington
   d. Curtis Joseph

7. This former Blues' center once commented, "The kids just aren't the same today."

   a. Craig Conroy
   b. Adam Creighton
   c. Doug Gilmour
   d. Terry Crisp

8. When discussing new composite sticks, Brendan Shanahan commented, "I tried using composite sticks last year, and I just couldn't feel comfortable."

   a. True
   b. False

9. This defender once stated, "I love telling myself jokes. I think I'm a riot."

   a. Doug Crossman
   b. Scott Stevens
   c. Dallas Eakins
   d. Dave Ellett

10. Which one-time Blues goalie once commented, "No one in Montreal learns how to skate. You're just born that way"?

    a. Jacques Plante
    b. Jacques Caron
    c. Martin Brodeur
    d. Yves Belanger

11. Bruce Affleck once described teammate Bob Gassoff as being "one of the most feared guys in the National Hockey League."

    a. True
    b. False

12. "I used to have a very good sixth sense, knowing exactly where someone was without seeing them," was a quote

by which rearguard?

a. Bryan Maxwell

b. Ric Nattress

c. Lee Norwood

d. Chris Pronger

13. Which Blue said this about their archrivals, "We hate Chicago and Chicago hates us and unfortunately he's on the other team and he's the big gun"?

a. Roman Polak

b. Mike Peluso

c. T.J. Oshie

d. Tyson Nash

14. "Everybody helps each other and never thinks about losing after the first or second period because we have 20 more minutes." This was T.J. Oshie describing the team's work ethic after an overtime win in 2013.

a. True

b. False

15. This netminder said, "It's tough to look great as a goalie. Most of the time, you're the one either letting in a goal or losing the game."

a. Ed Staniowski

b. John Davidson

c. Jake Allen

d. Rick Wamsley

16. After getting knocked out of the 2014 playoffs, which

Blue said to the media, "No offense to you guys, but these interviews are getting a little sickening to have in April and not in June"?

a. Ryan Miller
b. David Backes
c. Steve Ott
d. Vladimir Tarasenko

17. Which goalie shared his wisdom by saying, "Everything is nothing and nothing is everything"?

a. Ryan Miller
b. Curtis Sanford
c. Roman Turek
d. Chris Osgood

18. When told that teams that lose the first game of the Stanley Cup final usually lose the series, this Blues' player said, "That's why you guys do the stats and we play on the ice ... cool stats but it's not in our heads."

a. Patrick Maroon
b. Robert Thomas
c. Vladimir Tarasenko
d. Brayden Schenn

19. "Great sports city, underrated sports city in my opinion. The fans are great, and they never gave up on us all year." Who said this in the 2018-19 playoffs?

a. Ryan O'Reilly
b. Jordan Binnington
c. Coach Craig Berube

    d. Alex Pietrangelo

20. Former American President Ronald Reagan was quoted as saying, "I went to a fight the other night and a hockey game broke out."

    a. True
    b. False

QUIZ ANSWERS

1. C – Brett Hull

2. C – Wayne Gretzky

3. A – True

4. A – Brendan Shanahan

5. A – Grant Fuhr

6. D – Curtis Joseph

7. C – Doug Gilmour

8. B – False

9. B – Scott Stevens

10. C – Martin Brodeur

11. A – True

12. D – Chris Pronger

13. C – T.J. Oshie

14. B – False

15. C – Jake Allen

16. B – David Backes

17. A – Ryan Miller

18. C – Vladimir Tarasenko

19. D – Alex Pietrangelo

20. B-False

DID YOU KNOW?

1. During the NHL expansion meetings of 1967, league president Clarence Campbell remarked, "We want a team in St. Louis because of the city's geographical location and the fact it has an adequate building." Campbell was being pressured by the owners of the nearby Chicago Blackhawks to award St. Louis a franchise since they also owned the St. Louis Arena at the time. This meant they knew it could be sold with a team in the city.

2. Hall of Fame winger Brett Hull had this to say about his time in St. Louis, "You know what, I had 11 great years with St. Louis. My gosh, those are the best years of my life. And I will never, ever forget that."

3. Even though Wayne Gretzky is the all-time NHL leader in goals, assists, and points, the former Blue once said, "You'll never catch me bragging about the goals I score, but I'll talk all you want about my assists."

4. After getting run over by opposing players once too much for his liking in a game, Hall of Fame goaltender remarked to the media after the contest, "If I get run into again, I'm taking someone with me. I lost one knee. I'll take a head if it happens again."

5. This is how former Blue Brendan Shanahan once answered a reporter's question: "Is hockey hard? I don't

know, you tell me. We need to have the strength and power of a football player, the stamina of a marathon runner, and concentration of a brain surgeon. But we need to put all this together while moving at high speeds on a cold, slippery surface while five other guys use clubs to try and kill us. Oh yeah, did I mention that this whole time we're standing on blades 1/8 of an inch thick? Is ice hockey hard? I don't know, you tell me. Next question."

6. When speaking about his life as a professional athlete, former St. Louis netminder Curtis Joseph commented, "I think that when you are in the limelight it is part of your obligation to be a good role model. A lot of kids look up to you, and you are given a God-given talent, so it is your responsibility. It isn't hard to deal with. I never have to think twice about doing anything."

7. Doug Gilmour defied the odds by enjoying a Hall of Fame career at 5-feet-10-inches tall and weighing approximately 175 lbs. He was quoted as saying, "I heard it all the time, but I never looked at it that way. People that said I was too small were the ones that helped my career out. They were the ones that said I would never make it and they're the ones that made me fight that much harder."

8. After hanging up his playing skates and getting into coaching, Adam Oates remarked, "I can't be a hypocrite as a coach because as a player that's what I wanted. I wanted feedback, I wanted communication from the

boss. I showed up for work, you can yell at me if you want, but I want input. So that's the kind of coach I want to be."

9. St. Louis blue-liner Scott Stevens was known for his thunderous body checks and had this to say about his style of play, "What kind of respect do I get? ... Just because I'm a physical player, it's OK to come at me and do what you want? Hey, it's a hockey game. It's not figure skating. You know what? I can take a hit and I can give a hit. I don't care who it is. No one gets a free ride out there. I don't get a free ride, and no one gets a free ride from me."

10. Hall of Fame goalie Martin Brodeur's stint in St. Louis was very short at the end of his career but he explained his approach to the game by saying, "Goalies often react quickly to shots with no regard for what might happen to their body because we are trained to stop pucks first and ask questions later."

CHAPTER 4:

CATCHY NICKNAMES

QUIZ TIME!

1. Which player dislikes his nickname, "Tank"?

    a. Ivan Barbashev

    b. Justin Faulk

    c. Vladimir Tarasenko

    d. Zach Sanford

2. Former Blues' agitator Bob Kelly went by this nickname.

    a. Boss

    b. Thug

    c. Battleship

    d. Lightning

3. "The Blue Notes" is one of the team's alternate monikers.

    a. True

    b. False

4. Who is more used to their nickname "Snook" than his actual name?

    a. David Perron
    b. Ryan O'Reilly
    c. Vince Dunn
    d. Alex Pietrangelo

5. What was Gilles Marotte's nickname?

    a. Captain Crunch
    b. Jethro
    c. Bunny
    d. Shredder

6. Which of the following is not one of David Perron's nicknames?

    a. Perry
    b. DP
    c. P – Money
    d. DJ

7. Robert Bortuzzo is also called what name by his teammates?

    a. Zozo
    b. Bobo
    c. Tazer
    d. Bort

8. Jordan Binnington's hot start in the 2018-19 season earned him the nickname "Winnington."

    a. True
    b. False

9. David Backes earned this nickname because of his fighting ability.

   a. David the Goliath
   b. Super Backes
   c. Inglorious Backes
   d. Iron Fists

10. Which Blues forward is called "The Fixer"?

    a. Jacob de La Rose
    b. Alex Steen
    c. Robby Fabbri
    d. Zach Sanford

11. Brett Hull was known as "The Golden Jet."

    a. True
    b. False

12. Which Blues player was called "The Eel"?

    a. Gary Leeman
    b. Paul Cavallini
    c. Larry Keenan
    d. Camille Henry

13. Who was known as "Killer"?

    a. Scott Stevens
    b. Pavol Demitra
    c. Bernie Federko
    d. Doug Gilmour

14. Goaltender Curtis Joseph was nicknamed "Cujo" because he was in the movie of the same name.

    a. True
    b. False

15. What is ex-Blues' T.J. Oshie's nickname?

    a. OJ
    b. Ocean
    c. Osh
    d. Toe-shie

16. Which goaltender was known as Coco?

    a. Grant Fuhr
    b. Glenn Hall
    c. Mike Liut
    d. Brian Elliot

17. Which player is simply known as "Bo"?

    a. Tyler Bozak
    b. Jay Bouwmeester
    c. Sammy Blais
    d. Ivan Barbeshev

18. Which player is called "Neck" by his teammates?

    a. Nathan Walker
    b. Vince Dunn
    c. Alex Pietrangelo
    d. Carl Gunnarsson

19. What was Adam Oates' nickname?

   a. John

   b. Oatmeal

   c. Muffin Man

   d. Oatsey

20. Keith Tkachuk was nicknamed "Walt" after his father.

   a. True

   b. False

QUIZ ANSWERS

1. C – Vladimir Tarasenko

2. C - Battleship

3. A – True

4. B – Ryan O'Reilly

5. A – Captain Crunch

6. D – DJ

7. B – Bobo

8. A – True

9. C – Inglorious Backes

10. B – Alex Steen

11. B – False

12. D – Camille Henry

13. D – Doug Gilmour

14. B – False

15. C – Osh

16. A – Grant Fuhr

17. B – Jay Bouwmeester

18. C – Alex Pietrangelo

19. D – Oatsey

20. B – False

DID YOU KNOW?

1. The city of St. Louis has several nicknames, such as "The Gateway to the West," "The Gateway City," "Rome of the West," "The Lou," "Mound City," "River City" and "The STL." The state of Missouri is commonly known as the "Show Me State," "Cave State," and "Mother of the West." The hockey team itself is nicknamed "The Blue Notes," or simply "the Blues."

2. St. Louis goaltender Jake Allen, who has been with the club since the 2011-12 playoffs, goes by the nicknames "Snake" and "Jake the Snake." In addition, Hall-of-Famer and former Blues' netminder Jacques Plante was also known as "Jake the Snake." Plante played with the club from 1968 to 1970.

3. Former Blues' captain David Backes is known by several nicknames in the hockey world. These are: "Captain America," "Backs," "Inglorious Backes," and "Daddy Backes." The hard-working forward was a fixture on the St. Louis roster from 2006 to 2016 and played for the Boston Bruins and Anaheim Ducks in 2019-20.

4. Forward "Red" Berenson was known by his nickname throughout his hockey career with many former teammates and fans not knowing his real name was Gordon. Berenson played with St. Louis from 1967 to 1971 and got the nickname due to the color of his hair.

He was inducted into Canada's Sports Hall of Fame in 2005, the St. Louis Sports Hall of Fame in 2013, and the U.S. Hockey Hall of Fame in 2018.

5. Although former enforcer Craig Berube never played with the Blues during his 1,054-game NHL career his name will never be forgotten by the fans. Berube coached the club to its first-ever Stanley Cup triumph in 2019 after taking over behind the bench on Nov. 19, 2018. Berube is of First Nations descent and is known simply as "Chief."

6. Harry Steven Durbano went by his middle name Steve during his hockey career and earned a few nicknames along the way. Durbano was often called "Mental Case" and 'Demolition Durby" due to his erratic behavior both on and off the ice. He's the NHL's all-time leader in penalty minutes per game at 5.12 as he earned 1,127 minutes in just 220 regular-season outings. Durbano played with the Blues from 1972 to 1974.

7. After signing as a free agent, winger Radek Dvorak played just one season in St. Louis in 2006-07 and notched 10 goals and 27 assists in the full 82 games. The Blues missed the playoffs and Dvorak promptly re-signed with one of his former teams the Florida Panthers two months later. Dvorak was nicknamed "The Keyboard" after the computer keyboard.

8. Center Doug Gilmour starred with St. Louis from 1983 to 1988 and was nicknamed "Killer" by one of his Blues

teammates. Supposedly it was due to Gilmour's facial likeness to infamous American serial killer, Charles Manson. However, some believe he was given the moniker due to his physical play even though he weighed just 175 pounds.

9. Prolific goal-scorer Brett Hull was nicknamed "The Golden Brett" during his hockey career. The Blues' all-time leading goal-getter is the son of fellow Hall-of-Famer Bobby Hull, who was famously nicknamed "The Golden Jet." As of 2020, Brett was an executive vice president with the Blues.

10. Goaltender Manny Legace played with the Blues from 2006 to 2009 after signing as a free agent from Detroit. He must have been quite a character because he was known by several nicknames for some reason, including "Legs," "The Ferret," "Jimmy Buffett," and 'The God." Legace posted a .905 save percentage and 2.62 goals-against average with St. Louis in 140 regular-season games.

CHAPTER 5:

THE CAPTAIN CLASS

QUIZ TIME!

1. How many captains has St. Louis had as of 2019-20?

    a. 20

    b. 16

    c. 22

    d. 19

2. How many seasons was Brian Sutter the captain of the Blues?

    a. 5

    b. 7

    c. 6

    d. 9

3. Bob Plager was captain longer than his brother Barclay Plager.

    a. True

    b. False

4. Who was the franchise's first captain?

    a. Gary Unger
    b. Al Arbour
    c. Bob Plager
    d. Gary St. Marseille

5. How many points did captain Erik Brewer score in 2009-10?

    a. 9
    b. 20
    c. 15
    d. 13

6. Which player was captain from 1997 to 2002?

    a. Chris Pronger
    b. Eric Brewer
    c. Shayne Corson
    d. Dallas Drake

7. What is the highest plus/minus by a Blues' captain in a single season?

    a. +47
    b. +55
    c. +46
    d. +52

8. Al MacInnis was skipper of the Blues for a total of 83 regular-season games.

    a. True
    b. False

9. Who was the oldest captain in the team's history at the age of 40?

    a. Al MacInnis

    b. Wayne Gretzky

    c. Red Berenson

    d. Dallas Drake

10. How many seasons was Brett Hull the captain in St. Louis?

    a. 6

    b. 4

    c. 3

    d. 5

11. Brian Sutter recorded 254 penalty minutes in 1982-83.

    a. True

    b. False

12. Which captain recorded a minus -41 in 1978-79?

    a. Garry Unger

    b. Barclay Plager

    c. Barry Gibbs

    d. Red Berenson

13. How many players held the captaincy in 1995-96?

    a. 2

    b. 4

    c. 3

    d. 0

14. David Backes captained the team from 2011 to 2016.

    a. True

    b. False

15. How many goals did Bernie Federko score in his lone season as captain?

    a. 33

    b. 22

    c. 26

    d. 34

16. Who was the skipper during the 1989-90 season?

    a. Shayne Corson

    b. Garth Butcher

    c. Scott Stevens

    d. Rick Meagher

17. How many assists did Gary Unger earn in 1971-72?

    a. 18

    b. 29

    c. 34

    d. 41

18. Who is the only captain to play a full 82-game season as of 2019-20?

    a. David Backes

    b. Chris Pronger

    c. Alex Pietrangelo

    d. Brett Hull

19. How many penalty minutes did Eric Brewer serve in 2007-08?

    a. 91
    b. 79
    c. 104
    d. 108

20. The most assists a captain recorded in a single season was 56 in 2002-03.

    a. True
    b. False

QUIZ ANSWERS

1. C – 22

2. D – 9

3. B – False

4. B – Al Arbour

5. C – 15

6. A – Chris Pronger

7. D – +52

8. A – True

9. A – Al MacInnis

10. B – 4

11. A – True

12. C – Barry Gibbs

13. C – 3

14. A – True

15. B – 22

16. D – Rick Meagher

17. C – 34

18. A – David Backes

19. A – 91

20. B – False

DID YOU KNOW?

1. Since joining the NHL, the Blues have had 22 captains. They are Al Arbour, Garry Unger, Frank St. Marseille, Bob Plager, Barclay Plager, Jim Roberts, Red Berenson, Barry Gibbs, Brian Sutter, Bernie Federko, Rick Meagher, Scott Stevens, Garth Butcher, Brett Hull, Shayne Corson, Wayne Gretzky, Chris Pronger, Al MacInnis, Dallas Drake, Eric Brewer, David Backes, and Alex Pietrangelo.

2. The Blues had five different players act as captains in 1970-71: Garry Unger, Frank St. Marseille, Bob Plager, Barclay Plager, and Red Berenson. Unger, St. Marseille, and the two Plagers would also serve as captains the following season along with Jim Roberts. In 1972-73 Barclay Plager was appointed sole captain and Berenson took over for 1977-78.

3. The team listed no captain in 1976-77 and had three captains in 1995-96. Shayne Corson and Brett Hull started the 1995-96 season as captains and Wayne Gretzky was immediately handed the C when the Blues acquired him in a trade on February 27, 1996. Corson was then traded to Montreal in October 1996.

4. Wayne Gretzky's stint as St. Louis skipper was the shortest in team history as it lasted just 18 regular-season games. Gretzky tallied 8 goals and 21 points in

those contests and added 2 goals and 16 points in 13 playoff outings. The expected chemistry between Gretzky and Brett Hull never materialized and head coach Mike Keenan criticized Gretzky publicly. He then turned down a contract offer from the club and signed as a free agent with the New York Rangers.

5. Jim Roberts also had a short spell as captain of the squad. He was named captain before the start of the 1971-72 campaign but played just 26 games that season before being traded to Montreal. Roberts played defense and forward and was the first player St. Louis chose in the 1967 NHL expansion draft as they took him from Montreal. He then returned to the Blues for his final NHL season in 1977-78.

6. The longest-serving St. Louis captain was Brian Sutter. The forward was appointed before the 1979-80 season and held the job until the end of 1987-88, which was his final NHL season. Sutter played his entire nine-season career with the Blues with 303 goals and 636 points in 779 regular-season games. He added 21 goals and 42 points in 65 playoff outings.

7. Brian Sutter was also the most physical of the team's captains as he served 1,786 penalty minutes in his regular-season career along with another 249 minutes in the playoffs. Sutter recorded three straight seasons of over 200 minutes in penalties between 1980 and 1983, with seasons of 232, 239, and 254 penalty minutes.

8. Barry Gibbs' claim to fame was being drafted first overall 1966 by the Boston Bruins while fellow defender and Hall-of-Famer Brad Park went second. Gibbs was acquired by St. Louis in a December 1977 trade with Atlanta and was named captain for the following season. He was then traded at its conclusion to the New York Islanders. Gibbs notched 47 points in 127 regular-season contests with the team.

9. Eight different Blues captains served in the position for just one season or less. They were Jim Roberts (1971-72), Barry Gibbs (1978-79), Bernie Federko (1988-89), Rick Meagher (1989-90), Scott Stevens (1990-91), Garth Butcher (1991-92), and Wayne Gretzky and Shayne Corson (1995-96).

10. Seven former St. Louis captains were inducted into the Hockey Hall of Fame after hanging up their skates. They were defensemen Al Arbour, Chris Pronger, Scott Stevens, and Al MacInnis and forwards Brett Hull, Wayne Gretzky, and Bernie Federko. Arbour was inducted in the builder's category while the rest were enshrined as players.

CHAPTER 6:

STATISTICALLY SPEAKING

QUIZ TIME!

1. How many regular-season games did the Blues win in 2018-19?

    a. 44

    b. 46

    c. 47

    d. 45

2. How many 100-point seasons have the Blues registered as of 2019-20?

    a. 6

    b. 7

    c. 8

    d. 9

3. Brett Hull scored 72 goals in 1990-91, the team's single-season record.

    a. True

    b. False

4. Who leads the franchise in all-time assists with 721?

    a. Bernie Federko
    b. Brett Hull
    c. Brian Sutter
    d. Alex Steen

5. What was Ian Laperrière's shooting percentage in 1994-95, the highest in a Blues season?

    a. 24.1
    b. 24.5
    c. 23.2
    d. 23.0

6. How many minutes did Grant Fuhr play in the 1995-96 regular season?

    a. 3,960
    b. 4,127
    c. 4,261
    d. 4,365

7. Who recorded the most assists in a St. Louis season?

    a. 97
    b. 82
    c. 90
    d. 79

8. The squad scored 191 goals in its inaugural NHL season.

    a. True
    b. False

9. This player was assessed a club-record 306 penalty minutes in one campaign.

    a. Bob Gassoff

    b. Kelly Chase

    c. Reed Low

    d. Steve Durbano

10. What is the most goals allowed by a Blues netminder in one season?

    a. 213

    b. 209

    c. 250

    d. 235

11. The Blues' record in 1978-79 was 18-50-12.

    a. True

    b. False

12. Brett Hull holds the team record for points in a season with how many?

    a. 113

    b. 128

    c. 115

    d. 131

13. Which goaltender won the most games in a single season?

    a. Mike Liut

    b. Brent Johnson

    c. Curtis Joseph

    d. Roman Turek

14. Chuck Lefley and Larry Patey both notched a team-record 8 shorthanded goals in a season.

    a. True
    b. False

15. How many points did Doug Gilmour post as a rookie?

    a. 64
    b. 53
    c. 47
    d. 51

16. How many points did Vladimir Tarasenko notch in 38 games as a rookie?

    a. 31
    b. 25
    c. 19
    d. 27

17. The most power-play goals by a Blues player in a campaign is?

    a. 26
    b. 23
    c. 30
    d. 29

18. How many shots did goaltender Jake Allen face as a rookie?

    a. 453
    b. 378
    c. 346
    d. 422

19. Which player amassed 1,786 penalty minutes during his Blues career?

    a. Brian Sutter
    b. Barclay Plager
    c. Kelly Chase
    d. Barret Jackman

20. The most hat tricks recorded by a player in franchise history is 30.

    a. True
    b. False

QUIZ ANSWERS

1. D – 45

2. C – 8

3. B – False

4. A – Bernie Federko

5. B – 24.5

6. D – 4,365

7. C – 90

8. B – False

9. A – Bob Gassoff

10. C – 250

11. A – True

12. D – 131

13. D – Roman Turek

14. A – True

15. B – 53

16. C – 19

17. D – 29

18. C – 346

19. A – Brian Sutter

20. B – False

DID YOU KNOW?

1. When the 2019-20 NHL regular-season officially came to an end, the Blues had an all-time (won-lost-tied-overtime/shootout losses) record of 1902-1625-432-158 for 4,394 points and were 180-211 in the playoffs at the conclusion of the 2018-19 post-season.

2. The most points the Blues earned in a season was 114 in the 1999-2000 campaign with a record of 51-19-12. The fewest points was 48, which came in 1978-79 with a mark of 18-50-12. Those seasons also represent the club's high and low in winning percentage at .695 in 1999-2000 and .300 in 1978-79.

3. The all-time point leader for the franchise is center Bernie Federko with 1,073, which he posted in a club-high 927 regular-season games. He also leads the team in career regular-season assists with 721 as well as total goals on ice for at 1,408, total goals on ice against with 974, and total power-play goals on ice for at 566.

4. Winger Brett Hull is the all-time top Blue in goals with 527 and even-strength markers at 314. Hull is also the franchise leader with 195 power-play goals, 70 game-winning goals, 3,367 shots, and 27 hat tricks. Larry Patey leads with 23 shorthanded goals and Mark Hunter has the best career shooting percentage at 20.5.

5. Brett Hull holds the single-season records for goals with

86 and points with 131, while center Adam Oates holds the record for assists with 90. Hull's 57 even-strength markers, 29 power-play tallies, 12 game-winners, and 408 shots on net are all club single-season highs. Larry Patey and Chuck Lefley share the record for 8 shorthanded goals in a campaign.

6. On a career per-game basis with the club, Brett Hull leads in goals per outing at 0.71 while Adam Oates is tops for assists with 1.17 and also leads in points per game at 1.47. Both players also posted the best single-season marks in the same categories in 1990-91. Hull scored 1.10 goals per game while Oates recorded 1.48 assists and 1.89 points per game.

7. Let's not forget the most penalized St. Louis players throughout history. The most penalty minutes recorded in a season was 306 by defenseman Bob Gassoff in 1975-76. The most penalty minutes in a career was assessed to Brian Sutter at 1,786.

8. When it comes to goaltending, Mike Liut played 347 regular-season games with 151 wins, 133 losses, and 52 ties/overtime/shootout losses, all of which are career records. He also holds the records for 1,194 goals against, 10,359 shots against, 9,165 saves, and 19,973 minutes played. Brian Elliott is tops with 25 shutouts and a 2.01 goals-against average, while Jacques Plante's .931 save percentage is tops.

9. Grant Fuhr played the most games in a season for a goaltender at 79, while Roman Turek holds the record

for wins with 42. Jacques Plante and Brian Elliott share the mark for the best save percentage in a campaign at .940. Elliott's 9 shutouts is a team high as is his 1.56 goals-against average for a netminder who played at least 35 games. Mike Liut lost the most games in a season with 29.

10. Brett Hull's 67 goals, 117 points, and 102 games played are all Blues' playoff records while Bernie Federko posted the most assists with 66 and Brian Sutter recorded the most penalty minutes with 249. Mike Liut's 17 wins, 20 defeats, and 39 games played are goaltending playoff highs, while Jacques Plante leads in post-season shutouts with 4.

CHAPTER 7:

THE TRADE MARKET

QUIZ TIME!

1. What player did the Blues acquire from Detroit for Robby Fabbri in 2019?

    a. Jared Coreau

    b. Michael Del Zotto

    c. Andreas Borgman

    d. Jacob De La Rose

2. On February 26, 2012, St. Louis traded goalie Ben Bishop to which team for a second-round draft pick?

    a. Los Angeles Kings

    b. Ottawa Senators

    c. Winnipeg Jets

    d. Tampa Bay Lightning

3. The Blues traded Rod Brind'Amour to Philadelphia for Brent Sutter and Murray Craven.

    a. True

    b. False

4. How many trades did St. Louis make in 2009-10?

    a. 8
    b. 14
    c. 6
    d. 3

5. When the Blues acquired Brett Hull from the Calgary Flames, they also received which player?

    a. Craig Coxe
    b. Mike Bullard
    c. Scott Harlow
    d. Steve Bozek

6. Which player did the Blues give up to acquire Chris Pronger in 1995?

    a. Brendan Shanahan
    b. Doug Gilmour
    c. Craig Janney
    d. Petr Nedved

7. How many trades did the club make in 1995-96?

    a. 16
    b. 23
    c. 19
    d. 9

8. In 2010, St. Louis traded prospect David Rundblad to Ottawa for a first-round pick used to draft Jordan Binnington.

    a. True
    b. False

9. What package did St. Louis receive from Winnipeg for Paul Stastny?

    a. Erik Foley and 2019 first- and second-round draft picks

    b. Erik Foley and 2018 first-round and 2020 fourth-round draft picks

    c. Two future first-round draft picks

    d. Oskar Sundqvist and a 2020 second-round draft pick

10. In 2017, the Blues traded Jori Lehtera and two first-round draft picks to Philadelphia for which player?

    a. Brayden Schenn

    b. Petr Straka

    c. Taylor Leir

    d. Wayne Simmonds

11. St. Louis received a second-round draft pick from Washington for T.J. Oshie.

    a. True

    b. False

12. Which goaltender did the club receive from Montreal for Lars Eller and Ian Schultz in 2010?

    a. Chris Mason

    b. Manny Legace

    c. Marc Denis

    d. Jaroslav Halák

13. The Blue's first-ever trade, on June 6, 1967, was with this team.

    a. Detroit Red Wings
    b. Montreal Canadiens
    c. New York Rangers
    d. Toronto Maple Leafs

14. The Blues swapped Vladimír Sobotka, Tage Thompson, and Patrik Berglund to Buffalo for Ryan O'Reilly.

    a. True
    b. False

15. Who did the Blues send to Winnipeg to acquire Phil Housley in 1994?

    a. Nelson Emerson and Stephane Quintal
    b. Tom Tilley
    c. Ron Sutter
    d. Jeff Brown

16. St. Louis did not trade this player to Calgary in 1984 for Eddy Beers, Charles Bourgeois, and Gino Cavallini.

    a. Joe Mullen
    b. Terry Johnson
    c. Rik Wilson
    d. Mark Johnson

17. Who did the Blues receive from Carolina in 2019 for Joel Edmundson, Dominik Bokk, and a draft pick?

    a. Jakub Jerabek
    b. Justin Faulk

c. Jordan Schmaltz

d. Ryan Reaves

18. How many players did the Blues get from Calgary in exchange for Roman Turek?

   a. 6

   b. 5

   c. 4

   d. 3

19. From what team did the Blues acquire Keith Tkachuk for Mikhal Handzuš, Ladislav Nagy, and a draft pick?

   a. Phoenix Coyotes

   b. Winnipeg jets

   c. Atlanta Thrashers

   d. Dallas Stars

20. St. Louis acquired Hall of Fame goaltender Jacques Plante in a trade with Montreal.

   a. True

   b. False

QUIZ ANSWERS

1. D – Jacob De La Rose

2. B – Ottawa Senators

3. B – False

4. C – 6

5. D – Steve Bozek

6. A – Brendan Shanahan

7. C – 19

8. B – False

9. B – Erik Foley and 2018 first-round and 2020 fourth-round draft picks

10. A – Brayden Schenn

11. B – False

12. D – Jaroslav Halák

13. C – New York Rangers

14. A – True

15. A – Nelson Emerson and Stephane Quintal

16. D – Mark Johnson

17. B – Justin Faulk

18. D – 3

19. A – Phoenix Coyotes

20. B – False

DID YOU KNOW?

1. With Brett Hull being arguably the best Blue ever, his trade to St. Louis was an absolute heist for the club. Hull was playing in Calgary in 1987-88 with 26 goals and 50 points under his belt in 52 games. The Blues acquired him on March 7, 1988, along with Steve Bozek for goaltender Rick Wamsley and defenseman Rob Ramage. The rest is history, even though Bozek played only a combined 14 regular and post-season games with the team.

2. Acquiring center Adam Oates from Detroit was also a huge deal for the Blues, especially since he formed tremendous chemistry with Brett Hull and the duo was nicknamed 'Hull and Oates" after the famous singing pair Hall and Oates. St. Louis sent Bernie Federko and Tony McKegney to Detroit for Oates and Paul MacLean in June 1989 in what is considered one of the worst deals in Red Wing history. Oates holds several Blues' records and notched 286 points in 195 regular-season games.

3. The Blues traded Adam Oates in February 1992 after he had signed a four-year extension and then wanted to renegotiate the deal. St. Louis traded him to Boston instead for forward Craig Janney and defender Stephane Quintal. Janney scored 233 points in 186 regular-season games for the club while Quintal had a goal and 17 points in 101 games. Oates notched 499 points in 368

64

games as a Blue and finished his career with 1,420 points in 1,337 regular-season contests.

4. On Feb. 1, 1986, St. Louis dealt future Hall of Fame winger Joe Mullen to Calgary with defenders Terry Johnson and Rik Wilson for forwards Eddy Beers, Gino Cavallini, and rearguard Charlie Bourgeois. Mullen had scored 335 points in 301 games with the Blues and would end up with 1,063 points in 1,062 career games, win three Stanley Cups and two Lady Byng Memorial Trophies, and be named to three All-Star squads. Beers played just 24 games as a Blue before retiring due to injury, Bourgeois played 127 games and Cavallini notched 211 points in 454 outings.

5. The trade that brought Wayne Gretzky from Los Angeles in February 1996 also turned out to be disappointing because "The Great One" left to sign with the New York Rangers as a free agent just a few months later. St. Louis gave up Craig Johnson, Patrice Tardif, Roman Vopat, a first-round draft pick in 1997, and a fifth-round pick in 1996. They didn't give up much but, in hindsight, the first-round pick could have been used for Brenden Morrow, who would score 575 points in 991 career games.

6. Rod Brind'Amour was drafted ninth overall by St. Louis in 1988 and then traded to Philadelphia with fellow forward Dan Quinn in 1990-91 for forward Ron Sutter and blue-liner Murray Baron. Sutter posted 37 goals in 163 contests with the Blues while Baron was a solid

rearguard for seven seasons. Brind'Amour would win two Selke Trophies and a Stanley Cup and post 452 goals and 1,184 points in 1,484 games, adding 111 points in 159 playoff outings.

7. St. Louis and Calgary made another big deal in 1994 when the Blues acquired Al MacInnis and a fourth-round draft pick for fellow defender Phil Housley and two second-round picks. MacInnis, a seven-time All-Star, played 10 seasons for the Blues, won the James Norris Trophy, and tallied 452 points in 613 regular-season games. Both he and Housley ended up in the Hall of Fame.

8. Two other Hall-of-Famers were traded for each other when St. Louis and Carolina pulled off a deal in July 1995. St. Louis sent forward Brendan Shanahan to the Hurricanes for blue-liner Chris Pronger, who would become Blues' captain and score 356 points in 598 regular-season encounters with a +140 rating. Pronger, a four-time All-Star, also won the Hart and Norris Trophies with the team in 1999-2000 when he led the league at +52.

9. Center Ryan O'Reilly helped the Blues win the Stanley Cup in 2018-19 by being named playoff MVP and winning the Conn Smythe Trophy. He was acquired from Buffalo in July 2018 for Patrik Berglund, Tage Thompson, Vladimír Sobotka, and a first-round draft pick. O'Reilly led the Blues with 77 points in 2018-19 and added 23 points in 26 playoff games. He followed up in 2019-20 with 61 points in 71 games.

10. Let's visit one more St. Louis-Calgary swap. This one occurred in September 1988. The Blues shipped future Hall of Fame center Doug Gilmour to the Flames along with forwards Mark Hunter and Steve Bozek and defender Michael Dark for forwards Mike Bullard and Craig Coxe and defender Tim Corkery. Coxe played just 41 games with the Blues while Bullard skated in 20 and Corkery never played in the NHL.

CHAPTER 8:

DRAFT DAY

QUIZ TIME!

1. Who was the first player the Blues selected in the 1967 expansion draft?

    a. Jim Roberts

    b. Glenn Hall

    c. Noel Picard

    d. Don Caley

2. Which player did St. Louis select second overall in 1979?

    a. Gilles Leduc

    b. Mark Reeds

    c. Bob Crawford

    d. Perry Turnbull

3. St. Louis chose 31 players in the 1978 draft.

    a. True

    b. False

4. Of the eight players the Blues selected in 2016, how many were centers?

    a. 3
    b. 6
    c. 5
    d. 4

5. Who was the first player the franchise drafted first overall?

    a. Gary Edwards
    b. Alex Pietrangelo
    c. Wayne Babych
    d. Erik Johnson

6. How many wingers did the team draft in 2014?

    a. 6
    b. 7
    c. 8
    d. 9

7. Who was drafted in 2007 and played 148 NHL regular-season games?

    a. Lars Eller
    b. Anthony Peluso
    c. Ian Cole
    d. David Perron

8. Jaden Schwartz was drafted before Vladimir Tarasenko in 2010.

    a. True
    b. False

9. In which round did St. Louis draft Michal Handzus in 1995?

    a. 3rd
    b. 5th
    c. 2nd
    d. 4th

10. How many players has the franchise drafted as of 2019?

    a. 397
    b. 490
    c. 481
    d. 435

11. Gary Edwards is the goaltender selected highest by the Blues at sixth overall in 1968.

    a. True
    b. False

12. How many players did St. Louis select in the first round in 2007?

    a. 3
    b. 5
    c. 4
    d. 2

13. Where was goaltender Marek Schwartz drafted in 2004?

    a. 24th overall
    b. 10th overall
    c. 29th overall
    d. 17th overall

14. St. Louis drafted just two players in 1968.

    a. True
    b. False

15. Who did the Blues select 57th overall in 2001?

    a. Jay McClement
    b. Petr Čajánek
    c. Jeff Taffe
    d. D.J. King

16. Which legendary player did St. Louis draft in the 7th round in 1982?

    a. Cliff Ronning
    b. Ian Laperrière
    c. Rod Brind'Amour
    d. Doug Gilmour

17. Who was taken 62nd overall in 2003?

    a. David Backes
    b. Lee Stempniak
    c. Roman Polak
    d. Nikita Nikitin

18. In what year did St. Louis draft Bernie Federko?

    a. 1977
    b. 1979
    c. 1976
    d. 1978

19. How many players did the club draft in 1983?

    a. 2
    b. 1
    c. 0
    d. 4

20. Only two of eight players drafted in 1994 played at least one NHL game.

    a. True
    b. False

QUIZ ANSWERS

1. B – Glenn Hall

2. D – Perry Turnbull

3. A – True

4. C – 5

5. D – Erik Johnson

6. A – 6

7. B – Anthony Peluso

8. A – True

9. D – 4th

10. C – 481

11. B – False

12. A – 3

13. D – 17th overall

14. A – True

15. A – Jay McClement

16. D – Doug Gilmour

17. A – David Backes

18. C – 1976

19. C – 0

20. A – True

DID YOU KNOW?

1. The Blues were in turmoil in 1983 when Ralston Purina was attempting to sell the club and it looked as if it may be relocated to Saskatoon, Canada. Because of this, the team didn't send anybody to the 1983 NHL draft and forfeited its picks. It was the only time in NHL history that a club didn't participate in a draft.

2. After the 2019 NHL entry draft was completed, the Blues' had drafted a total of 481 players since 1967. They have also drafted several players through various intra-league and expansion drafts in the past.

3. When the NHL expanded from six to 12 teams in 1967, the league allowed the new clubs to draft unprotected players from the "Original Six" teams. The Blues selected goaltenders Glenn Hall and Don Caley as well as Jim Roberts, Noel Picard, Al Arbour, Rod Seiling, Ron Shock, Terry Crisp, Don McKenney, Wayne Rivers, Bill Hay, Darryl Edestrand, Norm Beaudin, Larry Keenan, Ron Stewart, Fred Hucul, John Brenneman, Gerry Melnyk, Max Mestinsek, and Gary Veneruzzo.

4. When signing future Hall of Fame blue-liner Scott Stevens in 1990, it ultimately cost the Blues five first-round draft picks. Stevens was a restricted free agent with Washington, and this was the compensation an arbitrator decided was fair after the Capitals declined to

match the Blues' contract offer. Stevens captained the Blues for a season and was then awarded to New Jersey as compensation when the Blues signed restricted free agent Brendan Shanahan.

5. The team had a chance to draft in 1967 but passed on their opportunity. This meant their first-ever draft pick was goaltender Gary Edwards in 1968, who went sixth overall. Edwards played just 64 minutes with the club before being claimed by Buffalo in the 1970 NHL expansion draft. Edwards went on to play 286 regular-season games in his 13-year NHL career.

6. St. Louis has drafted first overall just once in their history as of 2019 and also drafted second and third on one occasion each. They have had six top-five picks throughout the years as well as 13 top-10 selections. The Blues had no first-round draft pick on 22 occasions due to trades, losing picks to compensation, not showing up to the draft, etc.

7. In 2006, the team selected Erik Johnson first overall from the U.S. Under-18 National Development Program. He posted 91 points in 203 regular-season games before being traded to Colorado with the Blues' first-round draft choice in 2011 and Jay McClement for fellow blue-liner Kevin Shattenkirk, Chris Stewart, and a second-round draft pick.

8. The lowest-drafted Blue to play at least 400 regular-season NHL games was Mike Grier who was taken 219th

in 1993. He played 1,060 regular-season games over a 14-year career and posted 162 goals, 382 points, and 510 penalty minutes, with 28 points in 101 playoff games. He never played for St. Louis, though, as his rights were traded to Edmonton in 1995 along with Curtis Joseph for two first-round draft picks.

9. The lowest-drafted Blues' goalie to carve out a fine NHL career was Bob Froese. He was selected 160th in 1978 but was another player who never skated with the Blues; he signed with Philadelphia in 1981. Froese played eight seasons and shared the William M. Jennings Trophy in 1985-86 when he was also named a second-team All-Star, led the league in wins, save percentage, goals-against average, and shutouts.

10. The highest-drafted goalie was John Davidson, who was taken fifth overall in 1973. He played in just 93 games with the Blues before being traded to the New York Rangers in 1975. Davidson retired at the age of 29 due to injury, then entered broadcasting and won the Foster Hewitt Memorial Award and Lester Patrick Trophy. He was president of the Blues from 2006 until 2012, when he took the same job with Columbus. Davidson became president of the Rangers in 2019 and is also on the Hockey Hall of Fame selection committee.

CHAPTER 9:

GOALTENDER TIDBITS

QUIZ TIME!

1. Which goaltender played 347 regular-season games for the Blues?

   a. Grant Fuhr

   b. Curtis Joseph

   c. Mike Liut

   d. Jake Allen

2. What was Glenn Hall's save percentage in the Blues' first NHL season?

   a. .912

   b. .914

   c. .913

   d. .910

3. Martin Brodeur played the last two seasons of his career with St. Louis.

   a. True

   b. False

4. How many regular-season games did Grant Fuhr play in 1996-97?

    a. 73
    b. 67
    c. 59
    d. 62

5. What was Jordan Binnington's record in 2018-19?

    a. 22-7-2
    b. 24-5-1
    c. 26-3-2
    d. 25-2-3

6. Who had a .940 save percentage in 1968-69?

    a. Glenn Hall
    b. Robbie Irons
    c. Gary Edwards
    d. Jacques Plante

7. How many goaltenders played at least one game for the Blues in 2008-09?

    a. 6
    b. 4
    c. 5
    d. 7

8. Jaroslav Halák holds the record for the most shutouts in a season with 9.

    a. True
    b. False

9. Which goaltender had 28 penalty minutes in his six seasons with the Blues?

    a. Brent Johnson

    b. Greg Millen

    c. Mike Liut

    d. Curtis Joseph

10. How many goalies have played at least one game for St. Louis as of 2020?

    a. 51

    b. 41

    c. 61

    d. 71

11. Jake Allen had 6 shutout games in the 2015-16 regular season.

    a. True

    b. False

12. Phil Myre lost how many games in 1977-78?

    a. 28

    b. 35

    c. 19

    d. 25

13. How many saves did Curtis Joseph make during his time in St. Louis?

    a. 7,695

    b. 6,601

    c. 8,031

    d. 7,940

14. Rick Wamsley allowed 129 goals in 42 games in 1985-86.

    a. True
    b. False

15. Which goaltender lost 4 games in the 1969-70 playoffs?

    a. Seth Martin
    b. Michel Plasse
    c. Ernie Wakely
    d. Glenn Hall

16. Who allowed 193 goals in 1996-97?

    a. Bruce Racine
    b. Jamie McLennan
    c. Grant Fuhr
    d. Jon Casey

17. How many games did Roman Turek win in 2000-01?

    a. 24
    b. 16
    c. 30
    d. 42

18. How many assists did Curtis Joseph register in his 280 games?

    a. 20
    b. 17
    c. 15
    d. 18

19. What was Brian Elliot's goals-against average in 2011-12?

    a. 1.67

    b. 0.97

    c. 1.97

    d. 1.56

20. Eight goaltenders played at least one game for St. Louis in 2002-03.

    a. True

    b. False

QUIZ ANSWERS

1. C – Mike Liut

2. A – .912

3. B – False

4. A – 73

5. B – 24-5-1

6. D – Jacques Plante

7. C – 5

8. B – False

9. B – Greg Millen

10. D – 71

11. A – True

12. D – 25

13. D – 7,940

14. B – False

15. C – Ernie Wakely

16. C – Grant Fuhr

17. A – 24

18. B – 17

19. D – 1.56

20. B – False

DID YOU KNOW?

1. The Blues had used a total of 71 different goaltenders since joining the NHL until the conclusion of the 2019-20 regular season. Four of them have been inducted into the Hockey Hall of Fame: Martin Brodeur, Grant Fuhr, Glenn Hall, and Jacques Plante.

2. Of the Blues' 71 goalies, nine played just one regular-season game for the team while 11 of them played fewer than 20 contests. Mike Liut played the most at 347, between 1979-80 and 1984-985, and holds several club records and milestones. He was a two-time All-Star who won the Lester Pearson Award in 1980-81. Liut was traded to the Hartford Whalers in February 1985.

3. One of the netminders to play fewer than 10 games was Martin Brodeur, who appeared in the last seven outings of his 22-year career with the team. He signed as a free agent in December 2014 and retired a month later after going 3–3–0. Brodeur holds numerous NHL records, including wins (691), losses (397), shutouts (125), and games played (1,266). He's also the top-scoring goalie in league history with 3 goals.

4. The Blues have used five different goalies in a season on several occasions and the most they've used in one campaign has been seven. This occurred in 2003-03 when the following goalies all played at least one game:

Brent Johnson, Fred Brathwaite, Chris Osgood, Curtis Sanford, Tom Barrasso, Reinhard Divis, and Cody Rudkowsky.

5. Veteran Jacques Plante was acquired by St. Louis in the 1968 intra-league draft after retiring three years earlier. He shared the Vezina Trophy in 1968-69 with fellow Hall-of-Famer Glenn Hall with a 1.96 goals-against average and posted a 2.19 mark the next season. Plante was then traded to Toronto in the summer of 1970 and led the league with a 1.88 goals-against average in his first season there at the age of 41.

6. Glenn Hall was taken in the 1967 expansion draft at the age of 36 and played the final four seasons of his 18-year-career with St. Louis. He went 57-52-28 in 140 regular-season games, with a .917 save percentage and 2.43 goals-against average, and was 12-18 in the playoffs. Hall led the league in playoff appearances in 1967-68 with 18 and topped it in shutouts with 8 in 1968-69.

7. The Blues acquired Grant Fuhr in 1995 as a free agent and he played for them until being traded to Calgary four years later. He posted a 108-87-41 record in 249 regular-season games and went 15-14 in the post-season. He played a league- and club-record 79 games in 1995-96, when he went 30-28-16. Fuhr then played just two games in the playoffs that season.

8. The most wins in a St. Louis campaign is 42, by Roman Turek in 1999-2000. He went 42-15-9 with a sparkling

1.95 goals-against average and a .912 save percentage that season. He also led the league with 7 shutouts and shared his second straight William M. Jennings Trophy. Turek was acquired in a trade from Dallas before the campaign and was then dealt to Calgary just two years later.

9. Brian Elliott is currently the franchise leader in goals-against average at 2.01 and in shutouts at 25. He signed as a free agent in 2011, posted a 104-46-16 mark in 181 regular-season outings with a .925 save percentage, and was 14-17 in the playoffs. He led the league in goals-against average once as a Blue and in save percentage twice. Elliott was then traded to Calgary in June 2016.

10. The Blues soared from last place in the NHL to Stanley Cup champions in 2018-19 with a lot of help from 25-year-old rookie goaltender Jordan Binnington. He was called up from the minors in December, earned a shutout in his first NHL start, and went 24-5-1 over the rest of the season. His 24 wins is the club's rookie record and he's the first Blues rookie to record a playoff shutout. Binnington started every playoff game and holds the NHL record for 16 playoff wins in a season by a rookie.

CHAPTER 10:

ODDS & ENDS

QUIZ TIME!

1. What is the name of St. Louis' mascot?

   a. Blue

   b. Winston the Bear

   c. Louie the Bear

   d. Barry Blue

2. May 29, 2019, was the first time the Blues won a Stanley Cup final game. What was the final score?

   a. 4-3

   b. 2-1

   c. 4-2

   d. 3-2

3. Jimmy Roberts scored on the Blues' first-ever penalty shot attempt in the 1968 playoffs.

   a. True

   b. False

4. Who scored the first goal in franchise history against the Minnesota North Stars?

    a. Gary Melnyk
    b. Larry Keenan
    c. Frank St. Marseille
    d. Terry Crisp

5. Which coach amassed 709 points during his career with the Blues?

    a. Joel Quenneville
    b. Ken Hitchcock
    c. Brian Sutter
    d. Andy Murray

6. This player scored the club's first hat trick in November 1968.

    a. Ab McDonald
    b. Gary Sabourin
    c. Red Berenson
    d. Camille Henry

7. Against which goaltender did Vladimir Tarasenko score his first two goals in his NHL debut?

    a. James Reimer
    b. Jimmy Howard
    c. Antti Niemi Corey
    d. Corey Crawford

8. In the team's inaugural season, St. Louis finished in third place in the Western Division.

a. True

b. False

9. Against what team did netminder Jake Allen secure his first NHL win?

   a. New Jersey Devils

   b. Tampa Bay Lightning

   c. Minnesota Wild

   d. Detroit Red Wings

10. Who was the first team to defeat the Blues in 1967?

    a. Philadelphia Flyers

    b. Montreal Canadiens

    c. Pittsburgh Penguins

    d. Oakland Seals

11. Red Berenson once scored 6 goals in a game against the Philadelphia Flyers.

    a. True

    b. False

12. How many regular-season games did the Blues play at the St. Louis Arena?

    a. 1,094

    b. 1,100

    c. 1,080

    d. 1,071

13. What year did St. Louis move into the Enterprise Center arena (originally named the Kiel Center)?

a. 1994

b. 1995

c. 1993

d. 1992

14. At the end of 2018-19, the Blues held an all-time playoff record of 180-211.

    a. True

    b. False

15. What was coach Mike Yeo's record before being replaced by Craig Berube in 2018-19?

    a. 4-9-6

    b. 7-9-3

    c. 4-12-3

    d. 6-10-3

16. How many points did the team earn in 2014-15?

    a. 99

    b. 103

    c. 107

    d. 109

17. How many hat tricks had the Blues scored during regular- and post-season play by the end of the 2019-20 regular season?

    a. 161

    b. 176

    c. 160

    d. 153

18. How many general managers have the Blues had?

   a. 8
   b. 9
   c. 10
   d. 11

19. Since 2018, what is the Blues' official "victory" song played after each home win?

   a. When the Saints Go Marching In, by Louis Armstrong
   b. *Gloria*, by Laura Branigan
   c. *Song 2*, by Blur
   d. The Blues Have the Urge, by The Urge

20. Brett Hull scored 30 hat tricks with the Blues.

   a. True
   b. False

QUIZ ANSWERS

1. C – Louie the Bear

2. D – 3-2

3. B – False

4. B – Larry Keenan

5. A – Joel Quenneville

6. D – Camille Henry

7. B – Jimmy Howard

8. A – True

9. C – Detroit Red Wings

10. C – Pittsburgh Penguins

11. A – True

12. D – 1071

13. B – 1995

14. A – True

15. B – 7-9-3

16. D – 109

17. B – 176

18. D – 11

19. D – The Blues Have the Urge, by The Urge

20. B – False

DID YOU KNOW?

1. The Blues' first owner, Sid Salomon Jr., earned a reputation as being a players' owner because he often gave his players cars, treated them to vacations, and signed them to deferred contracts. The players felt they owed Salomon for his kindness and gave their best on the ice to show their appreciation. This led to the Blues reaching the Stanley Cup finals in their first three seasons.

2. Even though the Blues made the Stanley Cup final three years running starting in 1967-68, they failed to win a game in a final series. They were swept in four straight games by Montreal in 1968 and 1969 and suffered the same fate at the hands of Boston in 1970. The Blues didn't win a Stanley Cup final playoff game until 2019.

3. St. Louis boasted 10 players who scored at least 20 goals in the 1980-81 campaign. They were Wayne Babych (54), Jörgen Pettersson (37), Brian Sutter (35), Perry Turnbull (34), Bernie Federko (31), Mike Zuke (24), Tony Currie (23), Larry Patey (22), Blake Dunlop (20), and Blair Chapman (20).

4. The club's mascot is a large polar bear named Louie. He was first introduced to fans on Oct. 10th, 2007, and a few weeks later the name Louie was voted on during an internet poll. Louie can be seen at the Enterprise Center

wearing a team jersey with the No. 00 and his name on the back.

5. The Blues have had 26 head coaches throughout history: Lynn Patrick, Scotty Bowman, Al Arbour, Sid Abel, Bill McCreary Sr., Jean-Guy Talbot, Lou Angotti, Garry Young, Leo Boivin, Emile Francis, Barclay Plager, Red Berenson, Jacques Demers, Jacques Martin, Brian Sutter, Bob Plager, Bob Berry, Mike Keenan, Jim Roberts, Joel Quenneville, Mike Kitchen, Andy Murray, Davis Payne, Ken Hitchcock, Mike Yeo, and Craig Berube.

6. Lynn Patrick had three stints as head coach of the team while Scotty Bowman, Al Arbour, Leo Boivin, Emile Francis, and Barclay Plager each had two. The longest-serving coach was Joel Quenneville, who had 593 regular-season games behind the bench between 1997 and 2004. The shortest stint belonged to Jimmy Roberts at just nine games in 1997.

7. Former head coaches Scotty Bowman, Emile Francis, and Al Arbour are in the Hockey Hall of Fame as builders while Sid Abel and Lynn Patrick were inducted as players. Red Berenson, Brian Sutter, Joel Quenneville, and Ken Hitchcock were all honored with the Jack Adams Award as the NHL coach of the year while with the Blues.

8. As far as winning percentage is concerned, current coach Craig Berube is first in Blues' history at .657 in 134 games as of the end of the 2019-20 regular season. Lou

Angotti had the lowest at .281 in 32 games between 1974 and 1975. Berube was also leading in playoff contests at .615 with a 16-10 record, while eight coaches never made the playoffs and two others never won a post-season encounter.

9. The organization has had 11 general managers since Day One. In chronological order they are Lynn Patrick, Scotty Bowman, Lynn Patrick again, Sid Abel, Charles Catto, Lou Angotti, Sid Salomon III, Emile Francis, Ron Caron, Mike Keenan, Ron Caron again (interim), Larry Pleau, and current GM Doug Armstrong. Patrick, Bowman, Abel, Angotti, Francis, and Keenan also coached the team at one point.

10. Doug Armstrong was appointed general manager on July 1, 2010. Since then he has won the General Manager of the Year Award in 2011-12, the Stanley Cup in 2018-19, one conference title, two division titles, and has made the playoffs seven times. He's arguably the most successful GM in team history.

CHAPTER 11:

BLUES ON THE BLUE LINE

QUIZ TIME!

1. How many points did Alex Pietrangelo score in the 2018-19 playoffs?

    a. 16

    b. 19

    c. 14

    d. 20

2. Who was the highest-scoring defenseman on the 1992-93 roster with 78 points?

    a. Jeff Brown

    b. Garth Butcher

    c. Rick Zombo

    d. Stephane Quintal

3. Joel Edmundson led St. Louis with 239 hits in 2016-17.

    a. True

    b. False

4. Which defender had a team-high +22 rating in 1981-82?

    a. Kari Eloranta

    b. Jack Brownschidle

    c. Ed Kea

    d. Alain Vigneault

5. Who scored 4 power-play goals in 2014-15?

    a. Barret Jackman

    b. Alex Pietrangelo

    c. Kevin Shattenkirk

    d. Chris Butler

6. In 2011-12, how many rearguards blocked over 100 shots?

    a. 1

    b. 2

    c. 3

    d. 4

7. How many penalty minutes did Barclay Plager receive during the Blues' first season?

    a. 142

    b. 153

    c. 84

    d. 66

8. Al MacInnis was the third-highest scorer on the squad in 1998-99 with 62 points.

    a. True

    b. False

9. Who recorded 30 penalty minutes in the 2018-19 playoffs?

   a. Joel Edmundson
   b. Colton Parayko
   c. Jay Bouwmeester
   d. Robert Bortuzzo

10. This blue-liner had a minus-31 rating in 2005-06.

   a. Bryce Salvador
   b. Dennis Wideman
   c. Eric Brewer
   d. Steve Poapst

11. A total of 13 defenders played at least one game in 1987-88.

   a. True
   b. False

12. Chris Pronger tallied how many points in 1999-2000?

   a. 49
   b. 58
   c. 62
   d. 68

13. In his lone season with St. Louis, 1974-75, how many goals did Larry Sacharuk score?

   a. 22
   b. 14
   c. 20
   d. 16

14. Roman Polak blocked 103 shots and dealt 110 hits in 2012-13.

    a. True
    b. False

15. How many points did Blues' defenders tally in the 1971-72 playoffs?

    a. 5
    b. 10
    c. 7
    d. 13

16. Who had 188 shots on goal in the 2016-17 season?

    a. Colton Parayko
    b. Kevin Shattenkirk
    c. Jordan Schmaltz
    d. Brad Hunt

17. How many game-winning goals did Al MacInnis notch in 1999-2000?

    a. 8
    b. 10
    c. 4
    d. 7

18. What was Tim Bothwell's plus/minus rating in 1984-85?

    a. -16
    b. +27
    c. -9
    d. +9

19. Who was the only defenseman to play all 82 games in 2008-09?

   a. Roman Polak

   b. Barret Jackman

   c. Mike Weaver

   d. Jay McKee

20. During the 1977-78 regular season, eight defensemen had 10 or more points.

   a. True

   b. False

QUIZ ANSWERS

1. B – 19

2. A – Jeff Brown

3. B – False

4. C – Ed Kea

5. C – Kevin Shattenkirk

6. D – 4

7. B – 153

8. A – True

9. D – Robert Bortuzzo

10. B – Dennis Wideman

11. A – True

12. C – 62

13. C – 20

14. B – False

15. D – 13

16. A – Colton Parayko

17. D – 7

18. B – +27

19. B – Barret Jackman

20. A – True

DID YOU KNOW?

1. Six former Blues defensemen are enshrined in the Hockey Hall of Fame in Toronto, Canada. They are Scott Stevens, Al MacInnis, Phil Housley, Guy Lapointe, Chris Pronger, and Doug Harvey.

2. The highest-scoring defenseman in franchise history so far is Al MacInnis, with 452 points in 613 games and another 58 points in 82 playoff outings. MacInnis finished his NHL career with 340 goals and 1,274 points in 1,416 contests and added 39 goals and 160 points in 177 playoff games with St. Louis and Calgary. He also enjoyed seven seasons of at least 20 goals.

3. The longest-serving blue-liner in Blues' annals was Barrett Jackman after being drafted 17th overall by the club in 1999. He played 803 regular-season contests between 2001-02 and 2014-15 with a Calder Trophy tucked under his arm for his work in 2002-03. Jackman racked up 181 points and 1,026 penalty minutes before playing his final season with Nashville after signing as a free agent.

4. Defender Bob Gassoff played with the Blues from 1973-74 to 1976-77. He posted 58 points in 245 games with 866 penalty minutes, including a club-record 306 minutes in 1975-76. The rugged Gassoff lost his life at the age of 24 in May 1977 in a motorcycle accident while attending a

barbecue at the home of teammate Gary Unger. The Central Hockey League (CHL) created the Bob Gassoff Trophy after his death and the Blues retired his jersey.

5. Doug Harvey was known as one of the best offensive rearguards in the game during the 1950s and 1960s. He played his final season with St. Louis in 1968-69 at the age of 44. Harvey played 70 regular-season games and tallied 20 points. Before arriving in St. Louis, the 11-time All-Star was a six-time Stanley Cup winner with Montreal and won seven James Norris Trophies as the NHL's best defenseman.

6. Another ex-Montreal defender who ended up with the Blues near the end of his career was Guy Lapointe. He had made a name for himself as a four-time All-Star with the Habs and arrived in St. Louis via a March 1982 trade with the Canadiens. Lapointe played 62 games and posted 32 points before signing with Boston in 1983 at the age of 35. Lapointe tallied 622 points in 894 career games and added 70 points in 123 playoff encounters.

7. Brothers Bill, Bob, and Barclay Plager all played on the blue line with St. Louis. Bob and Barclay also served as captains and had their jerseys retired by the franchise. Barclay played his entire 10-season career with the team from 1967-68 to 1976-77, while Bob skated from 1967-68 to 1977-78 and Bill played from 1968-69 to 1971-72.

8. Current team captain Alex Pietrangelo has been with the organization since being drafted fourth overall in 2008.

He's a two-time All-Star who helped the Blues win the 2019 Stanley Cup and just concluded his 12th regular season in St. Louis in 2019-20. He's been a steady influence at both ends of the rink with 109 goals and 450 points in 758 games and 45 points in 83 post-season contests. He's a combined +85 in those games.

9. One of the Blues' veteran fixtures on the blue line from 1967-67 to 1971-72 was Noel Picard. The club obtained him in the 1967 expansion draft, and he chipped in with 58 points in 279 regular-season games with a +14 rating and 538 penalty minutes. Picard was claimed on waivers by Atlanta in November 1972 and he became a broadcaster for the Blues after hanging up his skates.

10. One of the most dependable offensive-minded Blues' defensemen over the years was Jeff Brown as he scored 0.89 points per game with the team. He came over in a December 1989 trade from the Quebec Nordiques and tallied 80 goals and 294 points in 329 games with 38 points in 42 playoff games. Brown was then traded to Vancouver in March 1994 in a multi-player deal that brought forward Craig Janney to St. Louis.

CHAPTER 12:

CENTERS OF ATTENTION

QUIZ TIME!

1. Which center posted 49 points in 2001-02?

    a. Doug Weight

    b. Ray Ferraro

    c. Jamal Mayers

    d. Mike Eastwood

2. How many goals did Bernie Federko score in 1983-84?

    a. 30

    b. 38

    c. 41

    d. 44

3. Gary Melnyk scored 50 points in 1967-68.

    a. True

    b. False

4. This center scored 12 goals during the 2018-19 playoffs.

    a. Jayden Schwartz

    b. Ryan O'Reilly

c. Brayden Schenn

d. Tyler Bozak

5. Gary Unger led the team with how many goals in 1976-77?

    a. 27

    b. 30

    c. 21

    d. 32

6. How many penalty minutes did Larry Patey rack up in the 1980-81 season?

    a. 99

    b. 105

    c. 123

    d. 107

7. This center had a minus-12 rating in 1982-83.

    a. Mike Zuke

    b. Ralph Klassen

    c. Blake Dunlop

    d. Alain Lemieux

8. Alexander Steen won 222 faceoffs in 2014-15.

    a. True

    b. False

9. How many points did David Backes register in 2010-11?

    a. 54

    b. 58

c. 62

d. 57

10. Which center had a +30 rating in 1999-2000?

    a. Mike Eastwood

    b. Marty Reasoner

    c. Pierre Turgeon

    d. Michal Handzus

11. Wayne Gretzky scored a combined 37 points in the regular and post-season with St. Louis.

    a. True

    b. False

12. Patrik Berglund had more hits than any other Blues' center in 2016-17 with how many?

    a. 138

    b. 155

    c. 122

    d. 167

13. How many centers played at least one game for the team in the 1978-79 campaign?

    a. 9

    b. 10

    c. 11

    d. 12

14. Ryan O'Reilly led the squad with 80 points in 2018-19.

    a. True

    b. False

15. Which center earned 28 assists in 2013-14?

    a. Maxim Lapierre
    b. Patrik Berglund
    c. Derek Roy
    d. Steve Ott

16. How many centers notched a hat trick in 2017-18?

    a. 3
    b. 4
    c. 2
    d. 1

17. How many career regular-season games did Marty Reasoner play for St. Louis?

    a. 88
    b. 105
    c. 86
    d. 95

18. Blues centers combined to score how many points in the 1989-99 playoffs?

    a. 26
    b. 33
    c. 37
    d. 18

19. Who scored 8 game-winning goals in 1974-75?

    a. Red Berenson
    b. Brian Ogilvie
    c. Garry Unger
    d. Wayne Merrick

20. Paul Stastny had 39 assists in 2016-17.

  a. True
  b. False

QUIZ ANSWERS

1. A – Doug Weight

2. C – 41

3. A – True

4. A – Jayden Schwartz

5. B – 30

6. D – 107

7. D – Alain Lemieux

8. A – True

9. C – 62

10. C – Pierre Turgeon

11. A – True

12. B – 155

13. D – 11

14. B – False

15. C – Derek Roy

16. A – 3

17. D – 95

18. B – 33

19. C – Garry Unger

20. B – False

DID YOU KNOW?

1. There are eight former St. Louis centers in the Hockey Hall of Fame. They are Bernie Federko, Doug Gilmour, Wayne Gretzky, Dale Hawerchuk Adam Oates, Guy Carbonneau, Vaclav Nedomansky, and Peter Stastny.

2. Vaclav Nedomansky was already a 12-season veteran in his homeland of Czechoslovakia when he defected to North America at the age of 30. After escaping from the Iron Curtain, he soon found himself in Canada. The center played just over three seasons in the now-defunct World Hockey Association (WHA) before joining the NHL with Detroit in 1977. Nedomansky played just the final 22 games of his NHL career with the Blues in 1983 after arriving in a trade with the New York Rangers.

3. Dale Hawerchuk was another Hall of Fame center who played briefly in St. Louis. The former first overall draft pick in 1981 signed as a free agent from Buffalo in 1995 and notched 13 goals and 41 points in 66 games. The team didn't make the playoffs and he was traded to Philadelphia before the season was over. Hawerchuk was a former Calder Trophy winner who compiled 518 goals and 1,409 points in 1,188 career regular-season games.

4. While we're at it, let's add Peter Stastny to the list of all-time greats who wound their careers down in St. Louis

and also defected from Czechoslovakia. Stastny arrived in St. Louis in March 1994 as a free agent but played just at the end of the 1993-94 campaign and the playoffs and six games the next season before retiring. Peter is the father of Paul and Yan Stastny, both of whom played with the Blues.

5. Bernie Federko was an unimposing figure off the ice but dominant on it. He was one of the most consistent and underrated players in the NHL after being drafted seventh overall in 1976. He topped 100 points four times in his career and had at least 90 points seven times between 1978 and 1986. Federko was the first player in league history to earn at least 50 assists in 10 straight seasons. The Blues' all-time leading scorer and longest-serving player was then traded to Detroit in 1989 and retired after one season.

6. One of the Blues' earliest stars was Gary Unger, who may be best known for his iron-man streak. The center played a then-NHL record of 914 straight regular-season contests from Feb. 24, 1968, to Dec. 21, 1979. He started the streak with Toronto and continued it with Detroit and St. Louis before finishing it with the Atlanta Flames. Atlanta coach Al MacNeil then benched Unger to end the streak. He played 662 regular-season games with the Blues, notching 575 points.

7. The Blues drafted Igor Korolev 38th overall in 1992 and he played 152 regular and post-season games before being claimed by Winnipeg in the 1995 waiver draft. He

played 795 regular-season games before leaving the NHL to play in Russia in 2004. Korolev sadly lost his life in 2011 with many others when the Lokomotiv Yaroslavl club's aircraft crashed after takeoff en route to a Kontinental Hockey League game in Russia. Korolev had turned 41 years old the day before the tragedy.

8. Unfortunately, another ex-Blues center-winger, Pavol Demitra, lost his life in the Lokomotiv Yaroslavl plane disaster when he was 36 years old. He was acquired in a 1996 trade from Ottawa and posted 493 points in 494 games with St. Louis, adding 43 points in 66 playoff outings. Demitra was chosen for three NHL All-Star Games with the Blues, won the Lady Byng Memorial Trophy in 2000, and led the league in game-winning goals in 2001-02. He was a three-time 30-goal scorer with the team and broke the 90-point barrier once.

9. As of 2020, former Blues center Pierre Turgeon was the highest-scoring retired player who hadn't been inducted into the Hockey Hall of Fame. The 1992-93 Lady Byng Trophy winner played 1,294 games in the NHL with 515 goals and 812 assists for 1327 points, along with 35 goals and 97 points in 190 post-season contests. Turgeon joined the team in an October 1996 trade with Montreal and posted 355 points in 327 games with the Blues with 45 points in 51 playoff matches.

10. Flamboyant Derek Sanderson was a long-haired star for the Boston Bruins but was more of a defensive specialist than a big scorer. However, he enjoyed his most

productive NHL season with the Blues in 1975-76 when he posted 24 goals and 67 points in 65 games. The former rookie of the year was traded to St. Louis by the New York Rangers early in the season and hung around for most of the next campaign before being sold to Vancouver. The controversial Sanderson had 33 goals and 89 points in 100 regular and post-season games before moving on.

CHAPTER 13:

THE WINGERS TAKE FLIGHT

QUIZ TIME!

1. Which winger scored 16 points in the 2018-19 playoffs?

    a. Sammy Blais

    b. Pat Maroon

    c. David Perron

    d. Nikita Soshnikov

2. How many points did Scott Young post to lead the team in 2005-06?

    a. 49

    b. 53

    c. 64

    d. 73

3. Pierre Plante was the only winger to play all 78 games in 1973-74.

    a. True

    b. False

4. Who took 397 shots on goal in the 1993-94 campaign?

    a. Brett Hull
    b. Brendan Shanahan
    c. Kevin Miller
    d. Igor Korolev

5. What was Vladimir Tarasenko's plus-minus rating in 2014-15?

    a. -1
    b. +15
    c. -2
    d. +27

6. How many points did Dickie Moore have when he led the team in playoff scoring in 1967-68?

    a. 9
    b. 12
    c. 14
    d. 17

7. Who tallied 38 assists in 1987-88?

    a. Gino Cavallini
    b. Tony McKegney
    c. Brian Sutter
    d. Mark Hunter

8. Gary Sabourin had four seasons with more than 40 points in St. Louis.

    a. True
    b. False

9. How many power-play goals did Brett Hull score in 1991-92?

   a. 25
   b. 20
   c. 27
   d. 29

10. Kelly Chase led the club in penalty minutes in 1997-98 with how many?

   a. 179
   b. 105
   c. 180
   d. 231

11. Paul Kariya contributed 66 points in 2007-08.

   a. True
   b. False

12. How many goals did Chris Stewart register in 2012-13?

   a. 5
   b. 10
   c. 18
   d. 17

13. Which winger doled out 276 hits in the 2014-15 season?

   a. T.J. Oshie
   b. Chris Porter
   c. Ryan Reaves
   d. Dmitrij Jaškin

14. Keith Tkachuk scored 18 power-play goals in 2003-04.

    a. True
    b. False

15. How many shots did T.J. Oshie block in the 2009-10 season?

    a. 44
    b. 58
    c. 62
    d. 65

16. This player scored 26 goals in 1979-80.

    a. Chuck Lefley
    b. Tony Currie
    c. Wayne Babych
    d. Blair Chapman

17. Which winger scored 2 shorthanded goals in 2016-17?

    a. Vladimir Tarasenko
    b. Scottie Upshall
    c. David Perron
    d. Magnus Pääjärvi

18. In 1969-70, which St. Louis winger posted 15 playoff points?

    a. Bill McCreary
    b. Frank St. Marseille
    c. Ab McDonald
    d. Larry Keenan

19. This winger banged in 28 goals in 2006-07.

    a. Bill Guerin

    b. Lee Stempniak

    c. Radek Dvorak

    d. Martin Ručinský

20. Brendan Shanahan chipped in with 102 points for the team in 1993-94.

    a. True

    b. False

QUIZ ANSWERS

1. C – David Perron

2. A – 49

3. A – True

4. B – Brendan Shanahan

5. D – +27

6. C – 14

7. B – Tony McKegney

8. A – True

9. B – 20

10. D – 231

11. B – False

12. C – 18

13. C – Ryan Reaves

14. A – True

15. D – 65

16. D – Wayne Babych

17. B – Scottie Upshall

18. C – Ab MacDonald

19. A – Bill Guerin

20. A – True

DID YOU KNOW?

1. The half-dozen former Blues wingers who made it into the Hockey Hall of Fame are Brett Hull, Brendan Shanahan, Paul Kariya, Dickie Moore, Glenn Anderson, and Joe Mullen.

2. Dickie Moore was 37 years old when he joined the Blues in a trade with Toronto in 1967-68 and hadn't played for over two years because he was retired. He twice led the NHL in points, three times in game-winning goals, and was a three-time All-Star who had won six Stanley Cups with Montreal. He scored eight points in 27-regular-season games in St. Louis and, once he found his legs, he led them in playoff scoring with 7 goals and 14 points in 18 games as they reached the Stanley Cup final. He then retired once more.

3. The undrafted Joe Mullen scored over a point per game with the Blues after signing in 1979. The winger tallied 335 points in 301 games with another 20 points in 20 playoff outings, including three straight seasons of at least 40 goals. In 1981-82, he became the first player in history to notch at least 20 goals in both the NHL and the minor leagues in the same season as he had 21 goals in 27 games in the AHL and 25 goals in 45 games as a rookie with St. Louis.

4. Brendan Shanahan was another Blues winger who produced over a point per game, as he registered 156

goals and 306 points in 277 outings and added 28 points in 26 post-season clashes. Shanahan signed as a free agent from New Jersey in 1991 and played until being traded to Hartford for fellow Hall-of-Famer Chris Pronger four years later. He led the NHL in shorthanded goals, shots on net, and hat tricks in 1993-94. Shanahan finished his career with 656 goals and 1,354 points in 1,524 games, along with 60 goals and 134 points in 184 playoff encounters.

5. High-scoring winger Paul Kariya signed a three-year, $18 million deal with St. Louis as a free agent in 2007 after leaving Nashville. He co-led the team in scoring in his first season with 65 points but suffered a season-ending injury in 2008-09 after notching 15 points in his first 11 games. He played one more season with 43 points in 75 games and then retired with post-concussion syndrome. Kariya tallied 989 points in 989 games in the league and tallied 39 points in 46 playoff games.

6. Glenn Anderson was another free agent signing; he joined the Blues after the 1994-95 NHL lockout was resolved. He contributed 26 points in 36 games in the 48-game season and added 2 points in 6 playoff outings before leaving the team. Anderson signed with Vancouver as a free agent in January 1996, was claimed on waivers by Edmonton three days later, and claimed by St. Louis on waivers six weeks after that. Anderson played the final 15 games of his Hall of Fame career in St. Louis and another 11 in the playoffs.

7. Inge Hammarström was one of the first Swedish players to succeed in the NHL after signing with Toronto, along with Hall of Fame defender Borje Salming in 1973. The winger preferred the finesse game to the physical one and scored 85 goals and 167 points for the Leafs in 292 games. The Blues traded for him in November 1977 and he tallied 72 points in 135 contests. Hammarström then became disillusioned with the NHL and returned to play in Sweden in 1979.

8. Winger Brian Sutter was well-known as a long-time Blues captain who scored 636 points in 779 games and racked up a club-record 1,786 penalty minutes. But many fans may have forgotten that two of his brothers also played with the team. Winger Rich Sutter played from 1990 to 1993 and posted 81 points in 250 regular-season games with 351 penalty minutes. Center Ron Sutter skated with the squad from 1992 to 1994 with 91 points in 163 outings and 236 penalty minutes.

9. Kelly Chase typically hit opposing players like a ton of bricks as he managed to accumulate 1,497 penalty minutes with St. Louis in 345 games, along with 100 minutes in 27 playoff outings. He played with the Blues starting in 1989 before being claimed by Hartford in the 1995 waiver draft. St. Louis reacquired him two years later in a trade with Toronto and Chase played until 2000 before retiring and becoming a Blues radio broadcaster. He won the King Clancy Memorial Award in 1997-98 for leadership qualities and humanitarian contributions.

10. When it comes to power-play specialists, Keith Tkachuk was one of the best between 2001 and 2010. The two-time All-Star scored 208 goals and 427 points in 543 games; 96 of those goals and 157 points came with the man advantage. He left the Blues via a trade with Atlanta in February 2007 but was reacquired in another deal just four months later. A total of 212 of Tkachuk's 538 career goals were on the power play as were 383 of his 1,065 points.

CHAPTER 14:

THE HEATED RIVALRIES

QUIZ TIME!

1. St. Louis was swept by which team twice in their first three Stanley Cup final appearances?

    a. Boston Bruins
    b. Montreal Canadiens
    c. Detroit Red Wings
    d. Toronto Maple Leafs

2. Who did the Blues beat to win a playoff series for the first time?

    a. Los Angeles Kings
    b. Minnesota North Stars
    c. Chicago Blackhawks
    d. Philadelphia Flyers

3. At the conclusion of the 2019-20 campaign, St. Louis had lost 156 of 319 regular-season games to the Chicago Blackhawks.

    a. True
    b. False

4. How many teams did the Blues go undefeated against in the 2000-01 season?

    a. 9
    b. 5
    c. 4
    d. 11

5. As of 2019, how many times have St. Louis and the Minnesota North Stars-Dallas Stars met in the playoffs?

    a. 14
    b. 17
    c. 12
    d. 13

6. St. Louis was eliminated from the playoffs three straight years (1996 – 1998) by which team?

    a. Phoenix Coyotes
    b. Toronto Maple Leafs
    c. Detroit Red Wings
    d. Edmonton Oilers

7. What was the score in a blowout win for the Blues against Florida on Oct. 5th, 2013?

    a. 9-0
    b. 10-1
    c. 7-0
    d. 8-0

8. St. Louis and Detroit engaged in an infamous brawl on March 17, 1991, known as "the St. Patricks' Day Massacre."

a. True

b. False

9. In 1990-91, the Blues scored how many regular-season goals against Toronto?

    a. 26

    b. 30

    c. 37

    d. 40

10. How many regular-season goals did the Blues tally against Pittsburgh in 1967-68?

    a. 33

    b. 29

    c. 31

    d. 40

11. St. Louis earned 5 points against eight opposing teams in 2006-07.

    a. True

    b. False

12. Which team outscored the Blues 16-6 in the 1995-96 regular season?

    a. Colorado Avalanche

    b. Calgary Flames

    c. Mighty Ducks of Anaheim

    d. San Jose Sharks

13. With how many teams did St. Louis tie at least 4 games in 1977-78?

a. 4

b. 5

c. 6

d. 7

14. St. Louis faced off against Toronto seven times in the playoffs in their first 51 seasons.

    a. True

    b. False

15. Which defunct team did the Blues defeat 8-2 on Jan.12, 1980?

    a. Minnesota North Stars

    b. Quebec Nordiques

    c. Colorado Rockies

    d. Hartford Whalers

16. The Blues have met this team six times in the post-season between 2000 and 2019.

    a. Vancouver Canucks

    b. Los Angeles Kings

    c. Dallas Stars

    d. San Jose Sharks

17. How many goals had Chicago scored against the Blues in 319 regular-season games as of the end of 2019-20?

    a. 1,044

    b. 910

    c. 977

    d. 1,032

18. What was the final score in Game 7 of the 2018-19 Stanley Cup final, when St. Louis won the Cup?

    a. 4-2
    b. 5-1
    c. 4-1
    d. 5-2

19. How many times have St. Louis and Boston met in the playoffs following the 2018-19 post-season?

    a. 2
    b. 4
    c. 3
    d. 5

20. St. Louis won 5 of their first 9 meetings with the Vegas Golden Knights, with their 4 losses coming in overtime/shootouts.

    a. True
    b. False

QUIZ ANSWERS

1. B – Montreal Canadiens

2. D – Philadelphia Flyers

3. B – False

4. D – 11

5. A – 14

6. C – Detroit Red Wings

7. C – 7-0

8. B – False

9. D – 40

10. A – 33

11. A – True

12. C – Mighty Ducks of Anaheim

13. D – 7

14. B – False

15. B – Quebec Nordiques

16. D – San Jose Sharks

17. A – 1,044

18. C – 4-1

19. C – 3

20. A – True

DID YOU KNOW?

1. The Blues entered the NHL in 1967 with five other teams, which meant natural rivalries were instantly formed. At the conclusion of the 2018-19 season, the club's playoff series records against the remaining teams stood at Los Angeles Kings 2-2, Philadelphia Flyers 2-0, and the Pittsburgh Penguins 2-1.

2. The team the Blues have faced the most in the post-season is the Dallas Stars, which entered the league with St. Louis as the Minnesota North Stars and relocated to Dallas in 1993-94. The Blues and Stars have met 14 times in post-season action, with the Blues holding the edge in series victories at 8-6.

3. The Blues vs Stars rivalry kicked off in 1967, when five of their 14 playoff series went the full seven games and four of those were decided in overtime. In addition, their 1998-99 second-round playoff series, which was won by Dallas, featured four overtime contests. Also, when the Blues won the Stanley Cup in 2019, they needed double overtime in Game 7 to eliminate the Stars. The Blues combined regular and post-season mark against the Stars franchise is 179-154-43.

4. St. Louis has met each of the "Original Six" teams in the playoffs at least once. The team's current series records against those organizations are: Boston Bruins 1-2,

Chicago Blackhawks 4-8, Detroit Red Wings 2-5, Montreal Canadiens 0-3, New York Rangers 0-1, and the Toronto Maple Leafs 3-2.

5. The Blues have met 19 different NHL teams in the playoffs. They have winning series records against six of them, losing records against 10 and even marks against the other three. They have won both series against Arizona and Philadelphia and the lone series against Winnipeg. They have lost all three series against Montreal and Vancouver and the lone meetings with Buffalo, Calgary, Colorado, Nashville, and the New York Rangers.

6. The two teams the Blues have had the most success against based on winning percentage are the two Florida clubs, the Panthers and Tampa Bay Lightning. They have never met either in the playoffs but their regular-season winning percentage against Tampa at the end of 2019-20 was 65.6 while the mark against Florida was 64.5 percent.

7. At the other end of the scale, the clubs that have given the Blues the most trouble since 1967 have been Montreal and the New York Rangers. St. Louis' combined regular and post-season winning percentages against those teams at the conclusion of the 2019-20 regular campaign were 32.4 against Montreal and 38.4 percent against the Rangers.

8. The Blues' biggest rivals are the Chicago Blackhawks because the teams and their fans simply don't like each

other and are separated by just 300 miles of highway. They have been in the same division since 1970 and games between the squads often featured numerous fights and penalties. All six of the Sutter brothers played in this rivalry for one of the teams. At the end of the 2019-20 regular season, Chicago led the series in wins at 152-121-35-11 and had a 35-38 edge in playoff victories.

9. The most infamous contest between the Blues and Chicago was the "St. Patrick's Day Massacre" on March 17, 1991, at the Chicago Stadium, when players were ejected and 278 penalty minutes assessed. In addition, Blues' defender Scott Stevens was suspended for two games while Chicago's Mike Peluso and Blues Kelly Chase were banned for 10 games each and both clubs were fined $10,000.

10. There was an intense Blues-Detroit rivalry during the 1980s when they played in the same division. The Wings beat the Blues in five games in 1988 to win the Norris Division final. In 1991, the Blues won the divisional semi-final after storming back from a 3-1 series deficit in games. The teams met three times in a row in the playoffs from 1996 to 1998, with Detroit winning each series. St. Louis' combined regular-season and playoff record against Detroit stood at 141-148-37 at the end of the 2019-20 regular season.

CHAPTER 15:

THE AWARDS SECTION

QUIZ TIME!

1. Who won the Lady Byng Memorial Trophy in 1989-90?

    a. Brett Hull

    b. Peter Zezel

    c. Adam Oates

    d. Paul Cavallini

2. How many points did the team have when it won the President's Trophy in 1999-2000?

    a. 115

    b. 114

    c. 111

    d. 113

3. Phil Goyette was the first Blues player to win a major NHL trophy.

    a. True

    b. False

4. Who was the first player from St. Louis named to the All-Star Game in 1968?

    a. Doug Harvey
    b. Al Arbour
    c. Jacques Plante
    d. Glenn Hall

5. How many times have the Blues won the Clarence S. Campbell Bowl as of 2019?

    a. 1
    b. 2
    c. 3
    d. 4

6. Who was the first coach in franchise history to win the Jack Adams Award?

    a. Red Berenson
    b. Joel Quenneville
    c. Ken Hitchcock
    d. Brian Sutter

7. As of 2020, how many former Blues are in the Hockey Hall of Fame as players?

    a. 27
    b. 30
    c. 24
    d. 18

8. Glenn Hall won the Conn Smythe Trophy with the Blues in the 1967-68 playoffs.

a. True

b. False

9. What award did Chris Pronger not win in 1999-2000?

   a. NHL Plus/Minus Award

   b. Ted Lindsay Award

   c. Hart Memorial Trophy

   d. James Norris Memorial Trophy

10. Who took home the Conn Smythe Trophy for the Blues in 2019?

    a. Brayden Schenn

    b. Alex Pietrangelo

    c. Jaden Schwartz

    d. Ryan O'Reilly

11. Jamie McLennan won the Bill Masterton Memorial Trophy in 1997-98.

    a. True

    b. False

12. How many goals did Jacques Plante and Glenn Hall allow to share the Vezina Trophy in 1968-69?

    a. 157

    b. 160

    c. 145

    d. 143

13. Who won the King Clancy Memorial Trophy and the NHL Foundation Player Award in 1997-98?

a. Al MacInnis

b. Pavol Demitra

c. Grant Fuhr

d. Kelly Chase

14. Brett Hull won more major NHL awards than any other Blues player.

a. True

b. False

15. Which player won the Calder Memorial Trophy in 2002-03?

a. Mike Van Ryn

b. Matt Walker

c. Barret Jackman

d. Christian Backman

16. How many Art Ross Trophies have the Blues won as of 2019-20?

a. 0

b. 1

c. 2

d. 4

17. Who won the William M. Jennings Trophy in 2000-01?

a. Jamie McLennan

b. Fred Brathwaite

c. Brent Johnson

d. Roman Turek

18. What season did Doug Armstrong win the General Manager of the Year Award?

    a. 2010-11
    b. 2011-12
    c. 2012-13
    d. 2014-15

19. Including 2019-20, how many division titles have the Blues won?

    a. 15
    b. 13
    c. 10
    d. 14

20. From 1975 to 1978, Garry Unger was the only player to represent St. Louis at the All-Star Game.

    a. True
    b. False

QUIZ ANSWERS

1. A – Brett Hull

2. B – 114

3. B – False

4. D – Glenn Hall

5. C – 3

6. A – Red Berenson

7. C – 24

8. A – True

9. B – Ted Lindsay Award

10. D – Ryan O'Reilly

11. A – True

12. A – 157

13. D – Kelly Chase

14. B – False

15. C – Barret Jackman

16. A – 0

17. D – Roman Turek

18. B – 2011-12

19. C – 10

20. A – True

DID YOU KNOW?

1. As of 2019, the Blues have won numerous individual and team awards since entering the NHL. They include the Stanley Cup (1), Clarence S. Campbell Bowl (3), Presidents' Trophy (1), Bill Masterton Memorial Trophy (2), Calder Memorial Trophy (1), Conn Smythe Trophy (2), Lady Byng Memorial Trophy (3), James Norris Memorial Trophy (2), Hart Memorial Trophy (2), Jack Adams Award (4), Frank J. Selke Trophy (2), Ted Lindsay Award (2), King Clancy Memorial Trophy (1), Vezina Trophy (1). and William M. Jennings Trophy (2).

2. The only major trophies the Blues' haven't won yet are the Art Ross for leading the league in points during the regular season and the Rocket Richard Trophy for leading the NHL in goals during the regular season. In addition, the Blues won the now-defunct Plus-Minus Award three times and the former NHL Foundation Player Award once.

3. The only Blues player who has been named rookie of the year was defenseman Barret Jackman in 2002-03. He tallied 3 goals and 19 points that season in the full 82 games. He also served 190 penalty minutes and possessed a +23 rating while averaging 20:03 of ice time per game.

4. The Conn Smythe Trophy for the MVP of the playoffs has been won by two Blues players. Goaltender Glenn

Hall was honored in 1967-68 when he led the team to the Stanley Cup final with a 2.43 goals-against average and a .916 save percentage in the post-season. St. Louis was swept in four games by Montreal, but each contest was won by just one goal. Center Ryan O'Reilly also won the Conn Smythe Trophy in 2018-19, when the club won the Stanley Cup. O'Reilly chipped in with a franchise-record 23 points in the post-season.

5. A trio of Blues skaters have been rewarded with the Lady Byng Trophy for their sportsmanship, ability, and gentlemanly conduct. Center Phil Goyette was named the winner for his play in 1969-70, followed by winger Brett Hull in 1989-90 and center Pavol Demitra in 1999-2000.

6. From 1927 to 1981, the Vezina Trophy was awarded to the team allowing the fewest regular-season goals. In 1982, it was given to the NHL's top goalie, while the William M. Jennings Award was introduced for the fewest goals conceded. Glenn Hall and Jacques Plante shred the Vezina for their work in 1968-69, while Roman Turek won the Jennings Trophy in 2000-01 and Brian Elliott and Jaroslav Halák shared it in 2011-12.

7. The Hart Memorial Trophy is awarded to the player deemed most valuable to his team during the regular season. Blues players to take this honor are winger Brett Hull in 1990-91 and blue-liner Chris Pronger in 1999-2000. In addition, forward Kelly Chase won the King Clancy Trophy in 1997-98 for leadership qualities on and

off the ice and humanitarian contributions in the community.

8. The Ted Lindsay Award is given to the player chosen the most valuable in the regular season by his peers in the NHL Players' Association (NHLPA). The two franchise winners in this category have been goaltender Mike Liut for his play in 1980-81 and Brett Hull a decade later in 1990-91.

9. The St. Louis rearguards to have taken home the James Norris Memorial Trophy as the best defenseman in the NHL so far have been Al MacInnis in 1998-99 and Chris Pronger in 1999-2000.

10. The league's best defensive forward is rewarded each season with the Frank J. Selke Trophy. St. Louis winners as of 2019-20 have been Rick Meagher in 1989-90 and Ryan O'Reilly in 2018-19. Also, forward Blake Dunlop won the Bill Masterton Trophy in 1980-81 for perseverance, sportsmanship, and dedication to hockey and netminder Jamie McLennan was so honored in 1997-98.

CONCLUSION

You've just read about half a century's worth of St. Louis Blues' memories in trivia and facts from 1967 to 2020. You've been able to re-live events and situations that took place every step of the way since joining the NHL in 1967 to winning the Stanley Cup in 2019.

We sure hope that all Blues fans have been entertained by the book and we've been able to educate some of the younger ones along the way.

The team has certainly entertained its fans since Day One by reaching the Stanley Cup final in its first three years of existence. It may have been a long time coming but the club finally made it back to the final series in 2018-19 and repaid its loyal supporters by capturing Lord Stanley's famous piece of silverware.

The book is meant to be a lighthearted and fun approach to the franchise's history with accurate facts, information, and trivia about numerous players, coaches, and general managers. We apologize if we have overlooked your favorites along the way, but the club has so much history to offer.

Passionate and loyal Blues fans may already know the answers to the questions, but some of the team's information may have slipped your mind, or there may be something you weren't too sure about. With this trivia book in hand, you can study the franchise's history and be well prepared to challenge fellow fans.

The St. Louis Blues have displayed a steely determination ever since joining the NHL and it's paid off with numerous divisional titles and a Stanley Cup championship. They're one of the most entertaining squads in the present-day NHL and they gained thousands of new fans with their persevering playoff performance in 2018-19.

Blues fans have proven over the years to be among the most faithful in the world of sports. Thanks for being one of them and taking the time to read the club's latest trivia fact book.

Made in the USA
Monee, IL
25 November 2023

47314600R00083